Conquer Your Heart Palpitations!

Discover the Unconventional Solution for Everlasting Relief

One Man's Journey from Agonizing Heart Palpitations to a Life of Peace and Tranquility

By Austin Wintergreen

Edgar Quicksand & Sons Book Publishing
Scottsdale, Arizona

ISBN Print: 978-1-7345809-3-8
ISBN Digital: 978-1-7345809-2-1

Interior Layout by Sandeep Likhar
Cover Design by Gus Tikno
Cover Photo by Joshua Earle / Unsplash.com @joshuaearle

www.AustinWintergreen.com

Note from the author

Dear Reader,

Thank you for your interest in this book. I greatly appreciate it. This is my second book, and I am incredibly happy to have found an audience whom I can help.

May I ask you a favor?

If you should come across any spelling or grammatical errors that bother you, could you email me personally before expressing your disappointment on Amazon?

I put a lot of effort into making sure this second book is free of errors, but some are bound to get through. In addition to hiring professional proofreaders, I've also meticulously proofread this book over nine times. However…

When I reviewed this book on Grammarly, there were still some mistakes! This can be so frustrating as an author. As a reader, it can be equally frustrating to read a book that has spelling and grammatical errors.

So, if you could let me know about any spelling or grammatical errors, I'd greatly appreciate it. This way, I can fix them right away, so others won't get frustrated. Here is my personal email address: AustinWintergreen@Gmail.com

Best wishes,

Austin Wintergreen

Medical Disclaimer

None of the information in this book is backed up by science, research, or anyone in the medical community. If you have a serious heart condition—including heart palpitations—you should seek professional medical help immediately. This book details the author's personal experiences with his opinions about heart palpitations. The author is not a healthcare provider. Not even close!

The author and publisher are providing this book and its contents on an "as is" basis and make no representations or warranties of any kind concerning this book or its contents. The author and publisher disclaim all such representations and warranties, including for example warranties of merchantability and healthcare for a particular purpose. In addition, the author and publisher do not represent or warrant that the information accessible via this book is accurate, complete, or current.

The statements made about products and services have not been evaluated by the U.S. Food and Drug Administration. They are not intended to diagnose, treat, cure, or prevent any condition or disease. Please consult with your own physician or healthcare specialist regarding the suggestions and recommendations made in this book.

Except as explicitly stated in this book, neither the author or publisher, nor any authors, contributors, or other representatives will be liable for damages arising out of or in connection with the use of this book. This is a comprehensive limitation of liability that applies to all damages of any kind, including (without limitation) compensatory; direct, indirect or consequential damages; loss of data, income or profit; loss of or damage to property and claims of third parties.

You understand that this book is not intended as a substitute for consultation with a licensed healthcare practitioner, such as your physician. Before you begin any healthcare program or change your lifestyle in any way, you should consult your physician or another licensed healthcare practitioner to ensure that you are in good health and that the examples contained in this book will not harm you. This book provides content related to physical and/or mental health issues. As such, the use of this book implies your acceptance of this disclaimer.

7 Suggestions to Get the Most Out of This Book

1. Develop a deep and strong desire to get rid of your heart palpitations forever.

2. Read each chapter with your full attention and a clear craving to get better.

3. As you read, take the time to reflect on how you personally relate to what's being said.

4. Highlight each import idea, so you can create a summary of important points.

5. Apply these principles at every opportunity and see yourself getting better.

6. Check in every week to see the progress you have made.

7. Have a firm belief that you are the one source for your cure.

Table of Contents

Preface

This book is about my experience in how I overcame my debilitating heart palpitations.

This book is deliberately void of facts and scientific studies. I wanted to make this book flow as easily and quickly as possible. Reference to scientific studies would only slow things down. It would also be an insult to your intelligence because you don't need facts to embrace what I say in this book. This book is solely about my personal journey with overcoming heart palpitations and the strategies I used to do that.

If you need facts and figures to convince you of what I am saying is true, then please put this book down and return it immediately. There is no third-party proof of what I am saying is correct. As the title suggests, what I am saying is unconventional and not talked about among doctors who study anxiety and heart palpitations.

You will encounter many alternative modalities that will make you question why you are reading this book. However, this is precisely where the magic lies. It's these unorthodox methods and strategies that do the real work in helping you overcome your heart palpitations. I know this approach has worked for me. When I talk to others who have cured themselves, they have applied similar principles.

The one overarching theme for me and my cure was to be more compassionate. By doing this, my heart began to calm down. I embraced more compassion by ensuring that I didn't vent my grievances out to the world.

One of the things that really helped was when I was commenting on online forums or writing book reviews on Amazon. In the past, I would often write bad reviews if I disliked the book in the least. I thought I was doing everyone else a favor. I was so annoyed that an author could write such nonsense—or if he should have a few spelling errors. I really wanted to "let him have it," so I wrote some nasty one-star reviews (I've since upgraded or removed my reviews).

Later, I realized this was doing me much more harm than it was doing good for other people. This crappy attitude was only making my condition worse. As you will see in this book, being angry at the world (and the many characters in it) will only make your situation worse.

Now, if I don't like a book, I just keep those thoughts to myself. I realize it's just my opinion. Everyone should have a right to form their own opinion without me dictating how they should feel. If only the world could be this way. As you will see in this book, this attitude that will be your CURE!

Introduction

What I discovered about my heart palpitations is that it's all in my head. Yes, there were some dietary changes and supplements that helped. But mostly, it was my mental attitude that made the most significant difference for me. My diet and supplements, for the most part, were just placebos. They gave me the feeling of being better. This cannot be underestimated.

Most books about handling anxiety talk about what to do. Do yoga, do breathing exercises, do whatever. They don't really talk about what not to do. This book is about what NOT to do. We all have bad habits that contribute to our anxieties and fears. This book will point them out, so you can recognize them and change them. Once you change them, you will be on the golden road to recovery.

A scary thing

Having heart palpitations is a terrifying thing, and often you think you are having a deadly heart attack. Heart attacks are caused by clogged arteries. We all know the statistics about heart attacks. Number one killer, etc.

But how do you overcome this fear of death? It's not easy. You don't just wake up one day and not fear that your heart is going to conk out. You could have a million doctors reassure you that your heart is excellent. Still, every time your heart skips, you start to doubt the professionalism of one million doctors. Maybe they all missed something.

Going after your problem head-on doesn't work. No amount of reassurance is going to help you that much. You must overcome this fear and anxiety by other means. That's what this book is about. It's about what they don't tell you when you pass all the exams, get the okay from your doctor's office, and pay for an expensive visit to a hospital.

Why should you listen to me?

I've been where you are now. I was a real victim of these devastating heart palpitations. I'm a real person who suffered just like you are suffering now. I'm not someone who did a massive amount of research just to write a book. This is my experience and my story. I've had severe heart palpitations for several years, and then I cured myself.

I saw the things I was doing in my life that caused my heart to act up the way it did. I see people on social media doing the same things, and it upsets me. I wish I could get through to them, but they will never listen. Don't be one of these people. Don't be someone who just wants to dabble in getting cured. Take a serious interest in getting your problem resolved. If you do, you will be rid of your heart palpitations. But you must take a serious interest.

Do you really want to get over your heart palpitations, or do you want to be a victim and complain for the rest of your life? Do you want to continue to have insufferable heart palpitations every day? Do you sit around hoping and wishing there was a cure, or do you want to finally get serious and actually cure yourself?

In this book, I will show you how the actions you take every day have affected your heart. I am incredibly passionate about helping you overcome your heart palpitations. I believe your heart palpitations and mine are a manifestation of something bigger than you or I could ever imagine. This is endemic in our society. You must listen to what I say in this book. It will help you in more ways than you could ever dream of.

Imagine not have any heart palpitations for the rest of your life. Imagine having all that agony and frustration left in the past. Imagine NOT thinking about your heart ever again. What would your life be like when you no longer have any heart palpitations? Would you work out more? Would you enjoy a nice glass of wine without worry?

You can eat what you want with worry. You could go for a nice walk in the woods without giving it a second thought.

I say these things because these are all things I enjoyed before my bout with massive heart PAC, PVC, and SVT attacks. I could no longer do simple things like roll over in bed. Since my complete cessation of heart palpitations, I can now take walks in the woods without worry.

What this book is about

People often ignore the hidden ways that bring about anxiety and heart palpitations. Many people will just tell you to not stress out so much or relax with soothing music or meditation. This doesn't really work. Why? Because you're not fixing the real problem. If you engage in the same daily habits, you will never get better.

-1-

Understanding the Pain That You Are Going Through

I understand the pain and discomfort you are going through. I have been there many times. I can tell you that things—if you want them to—will get better. Before I found a nearly 100% cure for my debilitating heart palpitations, I went through all the trauma that many people are going through right now.

Evenings

The evenings were often the worst. Whenever I went to bed, my heart would beat faster and faster. This made it impossible for me to even think about getting to sleep. Of course, this overthinking only made me breathe heavier and heavier. This, of course, would increase my anxiety and heart rate. Thus, the vicious cycle of heart palpitations, fear, and anxiety had begun.

I'm sure you've had the same experience. You've had heart palpitations before getting into bed one evening. From then on, you can't stop thinking about getting heart palpitations as you get into bed. If this has happened to you repeatedly, your bed has now become a source of anxiety. This, of course, triggers even more heart palpitations. Now, you are trapped in a vicious cycle.

This is precisely what I went through. I tried every little trick to get into bed, but nothing seemed to work. Every time I would approach my bed, my heart would thump around like an angry cat trying to get out of a pillowcase. Most times, I thought my heart was going to stop at any moment, and then that would be the end of me.

Often, I would stand next to my bed for about ten to twenty minutes, hoping my heart would calm down. It wouldn't. It would just jump all around. There would be fast beats, followed by slow rhythms, and then there would be totally random beats. It felt like a car running out of gas with that sputtering feeling. Nearly every time, I thought I was going to go into cardiac arrest and die right there, standing next to my bed.

Being so scared of dying and feeling the thumps in my chest, I would carefully and very slowly crawl into bed as if I were a three-toed sloth climbing up a tree. Often, I was so stealthy that I imagined that I was a cat burglar climbing in through a window to steal the crown jewels. I feared that if I made any herky-jerky movements, I would intensify my heart palpitations. I was doing everything I could to keep my heart calm, but nothing seemed to work.

Going to bed was often the worst time for me. Even if I got into bed, and everything was okay, my mind began to wander as I lay there in bed. I wondered how I was able to finally get into bed without any heart palpitations. What if my heart palps were just postponed? What if there was a sneak attack waiting for just the right moment? What if my heart thumps around in the middle of the night while I am sound asleep? What if…what if…?

On and on it went with the questions and the worst-case scenarios. It was awful. I'm sure you've had similar experiences. I know from reading the online forums that people have such a hard time when it comes to bedtime. These people just can't seem to get their hearts to calm down. It's an awful experience because bedtime is when you want to settle down and rest. Your mind may be restful (actually not, but we will talk about that in the coming chapters), but your heart isn't.

The good news is that I found a good evening routine to calm my heart—and eventually remove all traces of heart palpitations. We will talk about that in the chapters coming up.

Waking up

Waking up was hard, too. Often, I would wake up feeling great, and I didn't have any evidence of heart palpitations. I felt normal. I felt so normal that I didn't even check to see if I had heart palpitations. Out of sight and out of mind was the theory.

But then, several minutes later, as I began to think about my day, my dreadful heart palpitations began. It was frustrating. Just when I thought I was rid of these things, they were back. You probably had the same experience. One day you feel great, and then the next day, you feel awful. You don't know what you did to feel great, and you don't see what you did to feel terrible. It's tormenting.

The hardest part is you don't know what you did to get these heart palpitations. You start to question everything. Did I drink too much last night? Probably. Did I eat way too much for lunch? Possibly. Did I drink or eat too fast? Certainly. Did I get enough sleep, water, vitamins, etc.? Is my blood pressure too high or too low?

These are questions we ask ourselves. What brought on this nightmare? How do I make it stop? I will do anything to make these things go away; I can't stand it any longer. It's so heartbreaking (pun super intended).

Frustrations with doctors

I didn't always get a clear answer from my doctor. But that was not the only time I had visited a doctor about my awful heart palpitations. I went to several other general practitioners.

On one visit, my doctor convinced me I was having a heart attack. I had gone to a walk-in clinic because my heart was NOT beating fast or even intermittently. This freaked me out. My heart was beating a little slower than usual. Since I was used to a rapid heartbeat, this slower beat had me concerned. I let my anxiety get the best of me. Nowhere else to turn for immediate help, I went to a walk-in clinic that was highly rated for its resident doctor.

It was a cold winter day. The doctor asked me several questions about how I was feeling during my examination. I told her I was feeling a little pressure in my heart. I told her about all the heart palpitations I had in the past. She looked at me as if I said, "I see dead people." This highly rated doctor was utterly baffled by the words "heart palpitations." She didn't get this concept of heart palpitations or ectopic beats.

Anyway, she examined me further. She felt my hands. They were cold. She grew more concerned, and she said, "I think you're having a heart attack. You need to go to the emergency room right away."

Shit, I thought to myself. This is all need.

The doctor in the emergency room wasn't any more helpful. I'm still amazed that so many doctors and nurses are not aware of heart palpitations and ectopic beats. Everyone I spoke to about my heart palpitations kept asking me if I was scared or something. No, I didn't just run from a bear. I told them my heart palpitations would occur all day long. I wasn't scared all day long. What's wrong with these people?

After lying on a $3,000 hospital bed for an hour or so, the doctor came in and said there is nothing he could see that was wrong with me. He looked at my X-rays and said everything was okay. He said maybe it was acid reflux and gave me a Prilosec pill.

I'm sure you've had the same frustrations. You go to the hospital to get a workup and nothing. Nothing is wrong with you. Often, they don't even tell you that you have a PVC, PAC, SVT, etc. They just tell you that nothing is wrong with you as if you enjoy going to the emergency room at $3,000 a pop. It can be incredibly frustrating. I know. I've been there way too many times. Fortunately, I got past that, and I am now on the other side.

Holter monitor

I wore a Holter monitor for 24 hrs. I didn't catch anything as much as I hoped it would. This seems to be a common problem. You wear the thing all day (or longer) and nothing happens. You hope that you do have heart palpitations just to prove to you and everyone else that you really do have a physical condition. However, nothing happens. I will discuss later why this phenomenon occurs.

Sadly, the Holter monitor becomes even more frustrating because you set out to prove something. In my case, it only increased my heart palpitations afterward. I became frustrated with the whole thing. Just like a mechanic, a doctor cannot fix what he or she cannot see or reproduce. It becomes very frustrating—not to mention all the time and money spent (or wasted) conducting these experiments.

Don't worry, you are not alone. I have heard many stories of Holter monitors not catching anything. In fact, of all the stories I have listened to, only 5% of the people were able to catch something on their Holter monitor.

I can pretty much say the same thing about EKGs and echocardiograms. I've had several echoes and dozens of EKGs. Nothing was ever found. Nothing showed up that was a concern for my doctor. It was so frustrating because of all the time and money wasted on such endeavors. Meanwhile, I was still suffering from these debilitating heart palpitations. They were taking over my life.

I don't need to remind you that you have had the same experience. I've heard all the stories on social media. The numerous visits to the emergency room. The EKGs, the echocardiograms. The visits to your doctor, the cardiologist— the so-called "specialist." No one can make these things go away. No one! What. The. Fugg!

Surgery and drugs

I'm thankful I never went down this road and never had to. Sadly, I've read too many stories of people who have gone down this road, and they didn't get much better.

Many people have gotten ablation surgery to burn off electrical connections only to have their heart palpitations come back. I'm glad I know the reason why they come back, and I'm so happy it's as simple as changing a few bad habits.

In addition to surgery, I hear about so many people taking medications. These medications are hazardous, and I'm glad I never went down that road, either. They have many side effects and getting off them is nearly impossible. They change your brain chemistry forever. It's unfortunate. So very sad. I'm not convinced that surgery or drugs are a solution.

Conclusion

I know what you are going through. I went through the same things. Bedtime worries. The doctor visits. The $10 million hospital visits. The doctors look at you like you just escaped from a mental hospital. They think you get off on taking up their "precious" time. The surgery and medication options that seem promising, but you know they are risky.

I've been there. It's not fun—not by a long shot. Fortunately, I came out on the other side without spending thousands of dollars on therapies, drugs, or surgery.

You will, too, come out on the other side after you read this book. But I must warn you: many of the strategies I will talk about in this book have never been discussed by anyone in the medical community. Be prepared to be shocked and amazed by how I came to many of the strategies that have helped me become nearly 100% symptom-free for almost a year—after four years of torment. You'll read more about my story in the next chapter.

Key takeaways

- Evenings can be the worst
- Mornings can be difficult
- There is a reason why you don't get a reading when you want them
- Surgery and drugs are not the answer

-2-

My Story with Agonizing Heart Palpitations

If you read my first book, <u>My Heart Palpitations 97% Cured</u>, you know my story about my struggle with chronic and debilitating heart palpitations. However, for those who haven't read my previous book, I will give you a summary of my long battle with intolerable and often debilitating heart palpitations.

For about seven years, I had mild intermittent heart palpitations. I was in my early to mid-forties. During this time, I had gone to my general physician to inquire about these bothersome heart palpitations. After asking me a few questions and finishing her examination, she said these heart palpitations were nothing to worry about. It was all in my head.

I didn't think much of her comment at the time. While I wasn't happy with her answer, I wasn't upset either. I just walked away, feeling somewhat confident that I didn't have any real heart issues, such as artery blockages. Her prescription was to do nothing. It was, after all, in my head.

And it worked!

For six months straight, I didn't have any heart palpitations. I felt fine. I felt normal. My doctor's five words, "It's all in your head," worked! I felt great. I could play hardcore tennis without any problems. I could go to the gym and lift heavy weights without any issues. I could swim in the ocean waves and enjoy myself. Those damn heart palpitations were behind me. Yay!

Not a care in the world

I didn't do any research into my heart palpitations. They weren't consistent enough or bad enough for me to bother looking into it.

In fact, I didn't even know where to start. I'm not even sure if I called them heart palpitations at the time. I know I didn't refer to them as SVTs, PACs, AFib or anything else. I didn't know what those terms were. They were not in my vocabulary. To me, my heart palpitations were just weird flutters in my chest—not some ailment that had some medical terminology.

Since I didn't really have a grasp of what my problem was, I lived my life like I usually did. I ate terrible food. I drank heavily. I exercised to exhaustion. I didn't sleep well. I didn't stay hydrated. I filled my head with garbage from television news and radio talk shows like Rush Limbaugh and Howard Stern.

I had no idea about the ramifications of the heart palpitation cocktail I was creating inside my body. To me, it was business as usual. I just lived life normally. I figured if there was something seriously wrong with me, my doctor would have told me and given me some good ol' medicine. Medicine is good, right?

I played tennis, drank beer, watched TV shows late into the night. I got upset if my team didn't win, etc., etc. It was good times. I was living like nothing was wrong with me. I was in good health at the time, and I didn't care what I put into my body or my mind. I was in my mid-forties, so the world was still my oyster.

An increase in heart palpitations

Sixth months later, when I started to notice my heart palpitations again, I went back to the same doctor to inquire about them. This time my heart palpitations were a little more bothersome, so I was determined to get a better answer from my doctor.

Again, she said that my problem was probably all in my head. However, she agreed to give me a Holter monitor to see if we could catch these heart palpitations in action. I wore it for 24 hours. We didn't find anything. So much for that!

By this time in 2009, the economy had gone to shits, and no one was in the mood to do any hiring. I was doing a lot of traveling visiting family, and I was out of a job. I couldn't find work, and my wife was supporting the family while working at a job she hated.

We lived in a two-bedroom apartment that was comfortable. However, our dreams of buying a home went bust with the economy.

Since I was traveling so much, I was a bit nervous about getting on airplanes. I had a bad habit of watching airplane disaster shows on the Discovery Channel. I also watched real-life trauma shows on the Learning Channel. Whenever I went to the airport, my heart palpitations would increase. I was a very nervous flyer in those days.

By this time, I was getting a little frustrated with my dreadful heart palpitations. In the back of my head, I saw a connection between having anxiety—mostly related to flying—and my heart palpitations. However, I didn't see that the solution to my heart palpations was to reduce my stress. Like most Americans, my answer was at the bottom of a bottle—a pill bottle! I was looking for a prescription of some kind. Almost any prescription would do.

I'm not a big fan of prescription drugs, so I wasn't eager to get a prescription. However, my heart palpitations were such a problem that I just wanted to get rid of them as quickly as possible. I viewed any prescription as a cure. I wanted something that would fix my heart palpitations right then and there. Then I could move on with my life.

The way I looked at it was I would only need a prescription for a short period—kind of like taking an antibiotic—and then I could resume my life. I didn't view my heart palpitations as a chronic disease or ailment where I would be on medication for the rest of my life.

My doctor didn't have anything to give me. She still insisted it was all in my head. I was debating about seeing another doctor because I wasn't getting a solution to my problem. As it turned out, I had moved out of state shortly after; therefore, I had to get a new doctor anyway.

My heart palpitations did subside a little bit because "it was all in my head," so her advice came through again. The only time my heart palpitations really acted up was when I was at the airport or after I played tennis.

After my move, I was no longer traveling by plane, and I was no longer active in tennis. My heart palpitations just kind of went away—sort of.

The big SVT attack

It was several years later when I had a massive onslaught of heart palpitations. I thought I was going to die. I indulged in what I call *The Wendy's Heart Palpitation Cocktail*. This consisted of a double bacon cheeseburger, French fries, and Dr. Pepper. After I scarfed down that cocktail in about two minutes—maybe even less—I had a massive attack of heart palpitations. Later I learned this was an SVT event.

My heart was beating at about 170 beats per minute, and I could hear the blood squishing in my neck. I was in my father's home with no one around to help me. I thought about calling an ambulance, but for some reason, I didn't. I should have because I was getting dizzy.

Very sure I was going to die or collapse, I walked outside and stood in the driveway. I figured if I collapsed, someone would see me. And *they* would call an ambulance.

I really thought this was the big one—as in cardiac arrest. I had been out of shape for a while, and I had been very stressed due to moving and other events in my life. My father had passed away a few months prior, and I was cleaning out his house to get it ready to put it on the market to sell.

I had stopped playing tennis and stopped making regular visits to the gym. I had put on about 15 pounds of pure unadulterated Grade A fat. Finally, to put the nail in the coffin, I had *The Wendy's Heart Palpitation Cocktail*. (Poor Wendy's. They get all the blame in this story.)

Even though I thought this was a massive, fatal heart attack, I thought maybe it would go away—or at least, I was *hoping* it would go away. Yet, I didn't know what *it* was. Was it a clogged artery? Was my blood pressure too high? Did I get a snake bite? I didn't know, but I was hoping it would go away.

I prayed to God and asked God to forgive me for my sin of inhaling *The Wendy's Heart Palpitation Cocktail* in less than two minutes. I was genuinely sorry for what I did. Oh, so very sorry. Very sorry indeed. I promised I would never do it again. (And I never did!)

I guess someone answered my prayers (and my promise), because whatever *it* was subsided, and my heart began to regain its normal rhythm.

"What the hell was that?" I asked myself, standing in the driveway. "Holy shit!"

I quickly realized that *The Wendy's Heart Palpitation Cocktail* was the prime culprit. After all, it was a bunch of fat (burger, oil, bacon) combined with lots of sugar and caffeine. I'm surprised this didn't happen sooner. And to top it off, I ate the whole thing in less than two minutes. It was probably more like a minute and thirty seconds.

That was a big—and scary—one for me. Unfortunately, it wasn't the *last* big one. I had many more feeling-like-death-is-near episodes before I finally found my cure. After that big incident, I didn't have much activity in the heart department for a few years.

My viral infection

My full-blown case of chronic everyday heart palpitations didn't come until after I was admitted to a hospital for a viral infection.

While I was in hospital (that's how the British say it. In hospital. Not in *the* hospital. By the way, I'm not British. Why did I put that in there? Who the hell knows?). I was treated with all sorts of drugs and antibiotics.

After I was released from hospital, I started getting heart palpitations regularly. At first, I thought it was because I was so fatigued from fighting my illness. Later I blamed the sickness. Finally, I blamed the antibiotics. I think it was a combination of all of them: fatigue, viral infection, and antibiotics.

At any rate, after my illness and treatment, I developed chronic, unbearable heart palpitations for four years. Every single day, my heart would beat erratically, skip beats, and thump in the night. This would happen all day long every day. Hundreds of times a day, my heart would skip, bang around, stop, start again, and finally say, "Just kidding!" when I was sure death was near.

It was debilitating.

It was frustrating.

In search of a solution

It was during this time that I was on a quest to finally conquer my heart palpitations. I started to search the Internet to find a cure. I wasn't looking for a treatment because I didn't think it was anything that was to be cured. I was looking for a solution. I didn't see it as a disease. I just wanted my heart palps to just go away.

The first thing I read about was magnesium. I'm sure you've been down this road, too. I don't want to rehash what I wrote in my previous book. I will just list all the modalities that I tried during my four-year journey into heart palpitations:

- Magnesium
- Heart supplements
- Breathing exercises
- Tape over mouth while sleeping
- Meditation
- Staying massively hydrated
- Eating a plant-based diet

A lot of these worked and helped me on my road to recovery. But none of them really cured my problem 100%. My heart palpitations subsided only a little.

However, just like a screaming baby on an airplane, my tolerance for these went down the longer I was exposed to them—no matter how much they subsided. Although I reduced my heart palpitations by over 50%, I was still very frustrated because I wanted to get rid of them entirely. I just couldn't take it anymore.

I read numerous books and watched hundreds of videos. They were all accommodating in their own way. They brought my knowledge up from knowing nothing to knowing a lot more. However, none of them addressed the real cause—or what I believe is this real cause. I think it is the real cause because it was part of my solution. This brought me to nearly 100% cured.

This is what this book is about.

I also believe this is the right cure because for the past six months I basically abandoned every modality I had used before and written about in my last book. I rarely had a thump in my heart. Recently I had a few palps because of the end of year holidays. This being Christmas, I am literally eating one cup of sugar a day from cookies, cakes, M&Ms, and other treats. I'm eating a massive amount of meats and cheeses, and I've barely seen a vegetable. And my drinking is out of control. My sleep is okay. I still don't have a job, so stress is a factor.

To me, this is proof that my methods work if you want to be 99% cured.

I've been abusing my body for the past six months. I was on the Keto diet for 3 months. After that, I ate almost nothing but Lucky Charms, Cap'n Crunch, and Froot Loops for two meals a day. My wife was appalled. But after my Keto diet experiment, I was on a real sugar and carb bender.

I was consuming a massive amount of sugar, carbs, fats, etc. I was really going off the rails in terms of my diet. I was "out of control" as my wife likes to put it. But still no thumps. Did I find the magic cure?

Mind control is the answer

No palps. Why? Because I was able to gain control over my mind.

The Keto diet helped me get over my fear of fats. For nearly eight years, I had been on a plant-based diet where the fats were the enemy. Those fats were sure to clog my arteries and give me a heart attack. This stressed me out.

I went on the Keto diet with the attitude of "do or die." I ate lots of fat. Nothing happened. I didn't die. This helped me get over that fear of eating fats. When I was on a plant-based diet, I would eat a burger with lots of fear in my head and in my heart. This was stressful and was damaging to my mind and my heart.

Unfortunately, it took me a long time to really make the mind-body connection. Before that, I was doing all sorts of modalities to fix my problem. As I mentioned in my previous book, many of them worked for about two weeks and then didn't work anymore. I guess they were just placebos.

Why did I write this book?

In my last book, I touched upon a topic that would have doubled the size of the book if I really wanted to explore it fully.

During my journey to resolving my heart palpitations, I discovered something that no one really talks about. It really is "all in your head."

Of course, some people may have some real physical conditions. Those are the exceptions. However, for the rest of use, our heart palpitations are all in our heads. If your doctor, Holter monitor, emergency room physician has told you that there is nothing wrong with your heart, then this book is for you. This book will help you see that it really is all in your head (but not in the straight-jacket-rubber-room kind of way). This book will help you resolve your heart palpitations once and for all.

Does this book invalidate my previous book?

In my last book, I talked about a lot of remedies and modalities for resolving most of my heart palpitations. These remedies worked to some degree. However, I believe they worked because of the placebo effect. And let's be clear, that is not a bad thing. I'm a big believer in the placebo effect. If a placebo works just as good as the real thing, then what's the harm, right? Give me placebos all day!

Sadly, some people have the *medicine culture* deeply ingrained into their heads. These people are entirely against placebos and often cry, "You could be missing out on the real medicine!" This doesn't make sense at all. If a placebo works just as good as the medicine, then why do you need the "real medicine"?

Anyway, this book is all about finding a permanent cure by seeing what's messing with your head. This is the surprising discovery I made. I had so many things messing with my head that it made my heart go out of whack. Way out of whack.

I tried a lot of modalities like meditation and mindfulness. They weren't that effective if I didn't stop putting garbage into my head. This book is about seeing where the garbage is, and how and why you should avoid it. This garbage comes in many forms, such as the news, television, social media, friends, family, co-workers, etc. We will explore all of these in this book.

You could do all the meditation and mindfulness tricks all day long, but if you're still putting garbage into your head, you will always struggle. This is what happened to me. I was able to calm my mind and my heart to a certain degree. I was still putting garbage into my head. I was still feeding the monster, and that slowed my progress. It wasn't until I practiced the lessons in this book that my heart began to calm down.

It was a long journey. I wish someone told me as straight up as I'm telling you now. Many well-meaning doctors talk about "calming" solutions, but they only scratch the surface.

Many mindfulness and yoga gurus don't really know the problem we have with our heart palpitations. It's not their fault. If they never had heart palpitations, they would never know to address them.

This is why I am addressing this issue in this book. I believe this book is the only one of its kind. This book dives deep in how you can get over your heart palpitations by seeing exactly all the garbage you are putting into your head. I hope you get all the benefits out of this information that I did.

What is the cure like?

My life now is like a dream compared to my life living with heart palpitations. At age 51, I run up the stairs like a little kid instead of taking one step every 15 seconds like a 93-year-old man. I now go snow skiing after a ten-year absence. I'm fearless. I no longer worry about if my heart will skip a beat. I have the tools to stop any heart blip when or if they occur.

I can now roll over in bed without having my heart go into a wild rhythm, making me think I'm having a massive heart attack. Now, I flip-flop in my bed without a care in the world.

I can now go to the gym and lift heavy weights, breathe heavy, and not worry if I will have an SVT event. I love it! I couldn't have imagined living this way. I can now do cardio with few issues. I can walk or run on the treadmill, watch my heart rate go up, and not worry about an incident.

I no longer fear swimming in the ocean. This is something I missed dearly. When I was in the midst of my heart palpitations problem, I could barely swim in the ocean. I had a massive incident one time when I was just frolicking lightly. That scared me off swimming for a while.

Conclusion

I was where you are now. But I got over it. It wasn't easy, but I did it. But it didn't have to be so hard. If I had the right information, it would have been quite easy. This is why I wrote this book. I learned that it was all in my head, after all. There were no medicines that I could take. There are no exercises that I really need to do. I just needed to fix my head. And the best way to do that was to stop feeding it garbage. This is what this book is about.

Key takeaways

- I struggled with heart palpitations for four years
- I learned how to overcome my heart palpitations
- This book will show you how to overcome your heart palpitations
- I now have a life without heart palpitations

-3-

Don't Be Angry About Your Situation

As the title of this chapter suggests, you should stop being angry about your situation. When I say, "your situation," I mean two things. One is your actual heart palpitations, and the other is your current lot in life. First, I will talk about your heart palpitations.

Stop being angry about your heart palpitations

I know from personal experience that being mad about your heart palpitations will get you nowhere. When I first had my heart palpitations, I took them in stride. I looked for solutions and tried them out. I found magnesium; it worked for a while. I tried Hawthorn Berries; they worked for a while. I tried all sorts of supplements, and they all worked for a while—until they didn't.

Soon, I was getting very frustrated. I was no longer taking my heart palpitations problem in stride, and I was getting very agitated about my problem. I couldn't find a solution. What made things worse is that I was very close to a solution, but then I would relapse.

Had I hit a wall from the beginning, I wouldn't have been nearly as angry. I would have just accepted things as they were. However, in the back of my mind, I knew I did something to get myself into this mess. I just didn't know what it was. I thought the supplements were my solution. I thought I was deficient in magnesium or some other vitamin or mineral.

Maybe I was. But after taking three times the recommended dosage for several years, something wasn't working. I was getting better, but I still never had a full cessation of my heart palpitations. This is what made me frustrated and then eventually made me angry.

When I would be sitting at my desk and a heart palp came, I would bang my fist on my desk and yell out some expletive. Fortunately, I work for myself at home, so no one could hear me. Yelling out makes you feel better, right? I know I do.

However, it really didn't work for me for these dreadful heart palpitations. However, I just yelled out expletives anyway.

I didn't think getting angry and yelling out was really helping. But I didn't know it was hurting me either. It wasn't until I stopped getting angry and yelling out expletives, did I realize how damaging that activity really was to my heart situation.

Acceptance

Over time, I learned to accept and deal with my situation. It was a turning point for me, and I know it will be for you, too.

The more you can gracefully accept your situation, the better off you will be. I'm not saying you cannot continue to pursue a solution to your problem. You should. I'm just saying you shouldn't get angry and frustrated about it.

In one Facebook support group, many people were expressing their anger about their heart palpitations. I tell them exactly what I am telling you now. Unfortunately, they won't listen to me. I hope you do. Don't get angry. There is a solution.

You must accept your situation and be reasonable with your heart. If you are in any doubt about what I am saying here, then for one week, try your hardest to accept your situation. I'm not saying you should have a defeatist attitude. Just accept your condition for what it is.

You should accept it as if you have some other defect in your body. After a while, you begin to accept it. When I stopped worrying and getting angry about losing my hair, guess what happened? My hair loss ended! I'm not kidding. It has gone into remission. Thank goodness.

Anyway, when I learned to accept my heart palpitations, I felt them melt away. Let me be clear, this won't happen overnight. Once you start reducing your anger, you will feel something change over time.

Think of it as your calling

The way I started looking at my condition was that I was meant to have it, so I could tell others and be aware of my own mortality.

When I started to have a new attitude, I started feeling better. When I stopped seeing myself as a victim and started seeing myself as a conduit for a cause, I felt immeasurably better.

There is so little useful information about this condition that it can be frustrating. Most doctors shrug their shoulders and tell you it's all in your head. Many years later, I realized they were correct, but they didn't give me the pathway to overcome my condition.

I started to see myself as someone who could help others get better. I figured this condition had more meaning than just me being in bad health.

My own mortality

As you probably know, you will quickly realize your own mortality after you have many of these heart episodes. The first time I had a severe SVT episode, I was about 47 years old. Since I was in good health up until that point, I didn't question my mortality.

However, there are two ways you can question your mortality. I tried both ways, and one is by far better than the other. The first way was to see myself as dying young (if 47 can be considered young). Poor me. The other way was to see myself as living a damn good life, and if I die young, then so be it. I won't miss this place. If my family and friends miss me, they'll get over it soon enough.

It sounds rather grim, but thinking this way really helped me calm my anxieties. We don't really question our mortality if we are relatively young and have good health. I choose to think of it in a good way. It was a nice ride. If I should keel over and die, then that is fine with me.

I gave up resisting. I think that's the right way of putting it. In fact, I had watched a YouTube talk about this very thing. He said something about not resisting your heart palpitations. I didn't watch the whole video because I was already doing that.

It's important not to resist your heart palpitations.

Bring it on

You should have the attitude of 'bring it on!' It might sound scary at first. It might seem like you are conjuring up some underworld spirit to give you precisely what you are asking for. You don't want more heart palpitations, right?

But once you accept it and say, "Bring it on!", you will immediately feel better. You'll feel like you overcame your deepest fears. Having a massive SVT attack feels like you're gonna die. That's no time to say, "Bring it on!" However, resisting doesn't work either.

You may have thought that resisting and praying worked. I did, too. I thought staying calm and resisting was reducing the intensity of my heart palpitations. However, I found that I was still fearing the inevitable. I was resisting.

You must face your fears—your biggest fear of dying. Dying is no fun. But you must recognize that you're gonna die at some time, and it won't be fun. You may think now may be too soon. It will always be too soon. There will always be things you will want to live for. If you can honestly let go of that, you will feel so much better all the way around.

I started to accept my mortality and my imminent death. I truly accepted it. I was really, really tired of suffering with these heart palpitations. I was suffering just like you are now, and I just wanted out no matter what. I asked death to come to my doorstep. The fantastic thing is that I immediately felt death was further away than ever before.

As Sergeant Barnes said in *Platoon*, "Everybody gotta die sometime."

I'm not saying I'm a brave person for accepting my mortality. I'm not. In fact, I'm quite a chicken-shit when it comes to dying. However, the more that I think about the grand scheme of things, the less scared I am. The less frightened I am, the less my heart makes me feel like I am gonna die. It doesn't seem to make sense, does it?

The proof

Here's a little proof that having a bring-it-on attitude helps alleviate your heart palpitations. Have you had an EKG or wore a Holter monitor? What did you hope was the outcome of these tests?

If you're like most of us, you hoped that you would have a lot of skipped and erratic heartbeats, right? You wanted actual proof that it wasn't all in your head. You wanted evidence to show your doctor that you do have heart palpitations! You're not making this shit up.

So, what did you do during your tests? You told your heart to "Bring it on!"

What happened?

Nothing, right?

You got your EKG, and nothing happened. Nothing was picked up, no matter how hard you tried.

What about when you wore your Holter monitor for several days?

I know you desperately wanted to have a bunch of skipped beats. I know I did. I wanted real proof that I had heart palpitations. So, I told my heart to "Bring it on!"

What happened?

Nothing.

I've heard the same stories from people on forums, personal blogs, and books written about heart palpitations. Everyone has the same story. When they wanted their heart palpitations (for testing purposes, of course), they couldn't get a blip.

Some people went to extremes. One man drank a liberal amount of caffeine, drank red wine, purposely didn't hydrate himself, exercised heavily, and ate trigger-inducing foods. And still he couldn't get his 48 hr. Holter monitor to capture an event.

This is proof that when you have a 'bring it on!' attitude versus an attitude of resistance, your heart will behave nicely.

Don't exaggerate your condition

Of course, when you have an SVT attack and your heart is beating at 200 beats a minute, you think you're gonna die. It doesn't get any worse than that. You're not exaggerating.

However, some people on social media like to play the "poor me" pity game. They exaggerate their situation to get more sympathy. They paint a picture of how bad things are. It's not their fault. This is their deepest fears rising to the surface.

If you believe that you shouldn't say, "Bring it on!" because you might get what you asked for, then you should also believe the opposite is true. Essentially, you would believe that if you exaggerate your condition, you are getting more of what you are thinking, right?

These are all mind games. While telling your heart to bring it on is good, exaggerating your situation is bad.

The more you think badly about your situation, the worse off you'll be. If your condition is mild, and you exaggerate it, your body will align with what you are thinking and give it to you worse. Therefore, you should think positively and believe it's not as bad as you think it is. This is all part of the mindful tactics you should engage in.

When I have a heart palpitation, I would often say, "This is nothing. I've had this before. I can handle it." I don't believe I'm jinxing myself or conjuring up some evil spirit that will try to prove me wrong. No spirit is trying to prove you wrong. However, if you exaggerate your condition, your body will try to prove you right.

If you say, "This isn't bad," your body will follow suit. If you say, "This is the worst I've ever had," your body will follow suit.

Your body follows your mind. You must think only in favorable terms. When you say, "Bring it on!" you are moving in a positive direction. When you resist, you are moving in a negative direction. You don't want that negative energy around you.

This is hard for some people to believe, but this is how I cured myself nearly 100% of my heart palpitations. You must go with the flow. You will see how this all works throughout the book.

Your life situation

The second thing that you should stop being angry about is your life situation. When I first started getting severe heart palpitations, I was in a bad place and remained there for a while. I didn't like where I was living, and I was having a tough time holding down a job. I felt like the world was really screwing me over.

I was very angry about my situation. Unfortunately, it took me a while to realize that being mad about my situation wasn't helping me. It was only making things worse, and it aggravated my heart condition.

Getting angry about your life situation is what brought on your heart palpitations. You need to take a big step back and look at your life.

No matter if you're rich or poor, you can only view your life through *your* lens. Some people will look at you and think you have a great life. Some people will look at you and think your life stinks. But it doesn't matter how they view your life because you're the one who is living it.

Live on your terms

You need to only look at your life through your lens. That's the only way you should look at your life. If you have heart palpitations, you've been walking around like a zombie your whole life. I'm not kidding. When I woke up, I saw how good my life really is (even with all the bad shit that was happening to me). When I couldn't find a steady job right, I still looked at my life as pretty good.

I realized that I had been walking around like a zombie. I had been living life on everyone else's terms. I was living my life the way I thought everyone else thought I should live. My heart didn't like this and finally caught up with me. My heart screamed out, "Screw you, jerk!" Those are his words, not mine. Don't yell at the messenger.

My heart was screaming out to me that something was seriously wrong with how I was living my life. It wasn't saying that something was wrong with my life. It was *how* I was living my life. There is a big difference. I could have a shitty life, but if I have the right attitude about it, then I am living my life with a balance in my heart, and my heart would be okay with that.

There are so many things I could point out in my life that I could say aren't quite perfect, but I'm okay with that. If I watched the news or hung out on Facebook, I would start to see many more things wrong with my life. Therefore, I urge you not to watch the news. They only like to highlight what is wrong with your life. You need to focus on what's good about your life.

Stop comparing yourself to others

One of the things that get people wound up is looking at their life in comparison to other people.

People are constantly comparing themselves to someone else. It could be a coworker, a colleague, a classmate, a sibling, a family member, a friend, or even people on TV and radio. Or they are comparing their lives against some ideal that some other person has created.

For instance, I know many people want to have a Martha Stewart kind of lifestyle. They make themselves crazy, trying to live up to her ideal. What they don't realize is that much of Martha Stewart's life is fictional. She doesn't really do all those things that she claims to do. She has assistants helping her with many of her crafts, cooking, and entertaining. She just conveniently leaves that out when she writes a book or an article.

Manifest good things

Through the process of not being angry about my situation, I was able to improve my situation. At the time of my heart palpitations, I was living in a rental house because I couldn't get a mortgage to buy a home. My credit was terrible, and I didn't have a regular paycheck. I was a freelance writer, and projects came sporadically. I was really in a bad place, and then my heart goes haywire.

After I healed my heart through all the things I talk about in this book, I was able to manifest my dream home (or rather my wife's dream home). We were able to buy the exact home we wanted at a much lower price than many of the homes that were comparably not as good.

I absolutely believe that my not being angry about my lot in life, I opened myself to the good things in life. This is the kind of attitude you need if you want to overcome your heart palpitations.

Get better

If you want to heal your heart, you must let things go and stop being angry about your life. One book that helped me let things go is *The Untethered Soul* by Michael Singer. It was one of Oprah Winfrey's choice books. The main thing that Michael Singer talks about is letting things go.

It's vitally important that you let things go. If you keep things bottled up, you will continue to have heart palpitation issues. From my experience, you will continue to have the problems with your heart unless you really open your heart. You must go with it, and don't resist it. Don't *wish* your life was better. Appreciate what you do have and move on.

If you do choose a path of letting things go and living in the moment, you may come across a lot of "feel-good gurus." Tony Robbins is an example of what I mean. I think these gurus are well-meaning and have good intentions. It's good to listen to some of them occasionally. However, you must make sure you don't get caught up in all the "success" and "having a powerful life" stuff. It can start to make you feel bad about your situation.

You should aim to have a good life, not an extraordinary life. If you intend to have a good life and you appreciate all the things around, you will indeed have an exceptional life. However, a lot of these gurus make a lot of bold statements. You may follow some of their wisdom, and at the end of the day, you may ask yourself, "Is my life exceptional? It doesn't feel exceptional. Maybe I need to try harder."

Don't try harder. Don't try to grind it out. Go with the flow. Your heart will thank you.

My promise

I promise that if you start to let things go and not get so angry about your heart palps, your life and your condition will vastly improve. While you won't get a total overnight cessation of your heart palpitations, you will see improvements in your situation day by day. That I guarantee! But you must be patient.

Conclusion

Your mind is powerful. Your subconscious mind is even more powerful. Your subconscious mind runs your whole body without you having to think about it. If you poison your mind with negative thoughts, your body is going to react badly.

Some people get all sorts of reactions from negativity. They have skin issues, hair falling out, etc. You and I have heart palpitations. The best thing you can do going forward is to stop being angry about your situation. Not only about your heart palpitations but also about your life in general. Start to let things go and relax. Things happen because they happen. Stop resisting. Resisting will only make things worse.

Key takeaways

- Stop being angry about your heart palpitations
- Accept your situation gracefully and peacefully
- Think of your heart palpitations as your calling instead of being a victim
- Give up resisting your heart palpitations
- You should have the attitude of 'bring it on!'
- Accept things as they are

-4-

Creating an Identity Through Sympathy

When we seek sympathy from others, we run the risk of creating an identity for ourselves. In this case, it's the identity of being someone who suffers from heart palpitations. Unfortunately, I see this all too often.

I know a lot of people on Facebook who constantly talk about their condition or their other life hardships. In turn, they get a lot of "Oh, I'm so sorry." I understand there is a process of grieving when there is a loss, and you do want sympathy. When you have an occasional tragedy, seeking and getting comfort is good.

However, some people are chronically seeking sympathy for whatever ails them. This isn't healthy, and it won't make them better. When it comes to your heart palpitations, seeking solace will only prolong your condition. It won't make it better any sooner. Just look on social media. The ones who've had their condition for years are the ones who are the most active in these discussions. Don't you want to get rid of your condition like an old pair of smelly gym socks?

Facebook support groups

I had participated in a few Facebook groups for heart palpitations. I was hoping to find practical advice about my heart palps. There was very little advice. Just a lot of sympathy going on back and forth between members of these groups.

One woman who started one of these groups posts several times a day complaining about her heart palpitations. Whenever advice is offered, she ignores it. Whenever sympathy is thrown her way, she laps it up like a thirsty kitten.

Don't be this person. This woman will never get better and will always suffer. Deep down, she has no interest in getting better.

Creating an identity

Don't make this problem your identity. The more sympathy you get for your heart problem, the more you will identify with your problem. The more that you create an identity around this problem, the harder it will for you to cure yourself of your heart palpitations.

You should try to distance yourself from this problem. You should want it to go away and never come back—like a bad case of herpes. This is my second book on this subject, and it will probably be my last. I certainly don't want these heart palps to be my identity. I don't want to be the guy who has PACs or AFib (or whatever someone wants to call it).

I want to be about as far away from this problem as possible. I don't want sympathy. The good news is that I don't have this problem anymore. That's because I wanted to distance myself from it. But some people don't really want to get over it.

I remember one time when I was on the tail end of my problem, I had once exaggerated my problem so I could get sympathy from my wife. One morning, I was supposed to help my wife with some yard work. She wanted me to help her pull some weeds out of the plant beds.

The night before, I was up late watching movies. I slept in a little late, and I was groggy the next morning. My wife was upset that I had woken up late and missed our appointment to get this yard work done. I told her that I had been up late because of my heart palpitations. She sympathized and told me I didn't have to help her with the yard work.

Afterward, I felt terrible for exaggerating my problem. Had I been a different person (i.e., a shittier person), I probably would have used that sympathy for all sorts of occasions, and then I would have begun to identify with it.

It would have been an endless cycle, and I wouldn't get better. I learned early on that getting sympathy would only prolong my problem. After a while, I refused to talk to anyone about my problem. I didn't want pity; I just wanted to be done with it.

Fake sympathy

Often, it's just phony sympathy that you get because the people you are seeking sympathy from don't know what you are going through. They think an SVT episode just means your heart is beating fast as if you ran a 50-yard dash. What's the big deal? Or that PAC or PVC is just a flutter that everyone has occasionally. No big deal.

The people you try to get sympathy from will not have walked in your shoes. Unless you are part of a support group with people with the same problem, most people will have a tough time identifying with your suffering, so don't even try.

Whatever sympathy you are getting from strangers is probably fake and insincere. Not their fault. That's the way it is. They don't understand your problem.

Even when you are in a group of people with heart palps, their sympathy can rarely be genuine. They are suffering, too. They want comfort, also. They are more concerned about themselves than they are about you. It becomes a vicious cycle.

It's an addiction

Trying to gain sympathy for whatever problem you have is using the outside to heal the inside. It's no different than eating chocolate cake or getting drunk to mask your pain. It's not a long-term solution.

As I've emphasized throughout this book, the solution is within you, not outside of you. You must recognize that before you get better. If you continue to look outside of yourself for a solution, you will never truly get better. You may have masked some of the pain, and you may even feel cured, but you won't have cleared away the underlying problem.

It's like trying to seek out things that will genuinely make you happy. After you get that thing that you think will make you happy, you will only be satisfied temporarily. Soon that happiness will wear off.

Don't look outside of yourself for anything. Look within yourself to solve your problem. Don't look to other people or to things to make yourself happy. Don't look to doctors, support groups, or supplements to make your heart palpitations go away. They are all great for some advice and some direction, but at some point, you need to sprout your wings and know that you are the only one who can really solve this problem.

Rise above it and take responsibility

When you seek sympathy from others, you're telling the world and yourself that you've given up. You haven't really given up because you are reading a book about how to get over your heart palpitations. And that's good. However, you may still be performing the bad habit of seeking sympathy.

When you take full responsibility for your problem, you will begin to feel better. What does it mean to take responsibility for your problem? Very simply, it means that nothing outside of you is going to fully resolve this problem. Yes, supplements will help. Eating well and exercising will help. However, you won't be 100% healed until you fix what's sitting on top of your shoulders.

Once you accept that you are the only person who can help you, then you will be on your way to being fully cured. You must recognize that it is only you and your thoughts that are going to get you out of this mess.

This means taking full responsibility. Don't rely on doctors for their wisdom and their medicines. Don't rely on supplements. Don't rely on friends, family, or even strangers to give you sympathy. Take full responsibility for your problem.

In my last book, I wrote out a script that helped me with this kind of thinking. It went like this: "I have a strong and healthy heart, and I feel great."

Later I created a new script that I would have running in my head. It goes like this. "This is my problem and my responsibility. No one else's. I got myself into this mess, and I will get myself out."

This was my simple mantra. It worked very well for me. Come up with a simple mantra to remind yourself that you are taking full responsibility for your problem.

Support groups are more damaging than you know

Not only will you get fake sympathy from support groups, but you will also be a participant in the contest of "who's got it worse." Is this a game you really want to win?

I've read the threads on these support groups, and it's unfortunate. In trying to offer sympathy, people will try to one-up each other. If you don't have it bad, someone will remind you how bad you could have it. Fun, right?

And if you don't have it bad, do you even feel worthy of being in the group and moaning? Maybe you should come back next week when you feel worse. Then, there will be justification for you to be worthy.

This kind of stuff goes on all the time. It's easy for me to see because I'm nearly 100% cured. But to someone who is still in the throes of their heart palpitations, it's not so easy to see the contest of one-upmanship going on.

Your best bet is to leave the group. You will only get better when you do. I promise you that. And think about the organizer of the group. Does she really want to get better? After all, her identity is wrapped up in being the organizer of the heart palpitations group and a fellow sufferer. If she gets cured, she will lose her status as a fellow sufferer.

Yes, she will gain a new identity as someone who has conquered her heart palpitations. However, she will have to create a whole new group of people who want to cure their heart palpitations. Her current group is filled with people who just want sympathy. I'm no Psyche major, but I know this well.

You must take full responsibility for your cure. Looking to support groups for sympathy is not taking responsibility. You are just putting the emphasis on others to fix your problem. Seeking comfort will not fix your problem. Only you can fix your problem.

Asking supporting questions

A lot of people ask advice on various topics such as magnesium and other modalities.

Many of the answers are:

> "I don't know. I would be too scared to try that."
> "That doesn't work. Don't bother."

"If you want to make things worse, do this…"

Do these kinds of exchanges help? Do they clear up any sort of confusion for you? Not really.

Do you want to make things worse for yourself? Join a heart palpitations support group. If you think about it, a group like that needs more victims.

Mess with your head

Here's a conversation I heard on one of these support groups.

> Betty Cummings*: "I take [magnesium] 3 x per day. Please make sure you are 2 hours away from all dairy; otherwise, you'll take it for nothing. Works great for me."

> Anamtha Willard*: "I didn't know that, I heard it should be taken together, I probably heard wrong, lol'"

Is this the kind of confusing crap you need to be filling your head with? I could write a whole book about all the wrong, erroneous, and contradictory advice you would get from these support groups.

Stay away, take responsibility, and seek out real advice from experts or people who have been in your shoes and have gotten over it. Yes, you are doing that right now by reading this book. That's good. Keep it up. You will get better, and this book will make that happen faster.

---

* These are completely made-up names, but the exchange is real.

Conclusion

The key to overcoming your heart palpitations is taking responsibility for your condition and your cure. A big part of that is not acting like a victim of your condition and your circumstance. When you tell people about your situation (other than your doctor) by posting on forums, you are perpetuating your victimhood. This will only prolong your suffering.

Facebook groups are fine for some Q&A and some suggestions, but don't make it habit of relying on these groups as your only source of information.

Key takeaways

- Don't try to gain sympathy for your heart palpitations
- Don't make this problem your identity
- Other people won't really understand what you are going through
- Take responsibility for your solution
- Limit time in support groups

-5-

Engaging in this Daily Habit Will Get You Nowhere

Stop complaining already!

Complaining has become an American pastime. It's a bad habit that we all engage in daily. I know I do it… a lot. I've gotten better at reducing my complaining, but I still do it. However, I make a daily effort to curb my complaining because I know it's not good for me, and it won't get me anywhere.

It seems that the more our lives get better, the more we complain, right?

We complain about…

- Our iPhone short battery life
- Netflix removed a movie
- Slow internet service
- Slightly tarnished/imperfect produce at the grocery store
- Television remote not working
- GPS giving wrong directions
- Boring… vacations, movies, concerts, company, etc.
- Lack of almond milk…gluten-free…dairy-free…low carb, etc.

- Advertising pop-ups
- Google, Amazon, Facebook, etc. knows everything about me (but they're still free)
- Weathermen/women getting the forecast wrong
- Traveling, too many people, rides suck
- TSA/airports
- Coffee

Are you guilty of some or all of these? I know I am. That's how I came up with this list. However, I try to put things into perspective.

Can you imagine if you lived on a deserted island with just a loincloth and a life's supply of coconuts? Would you have much to complain about? The more stuff we have, the more things we complain about. It's the stuff!

Recently, my wife quipped that there was nothing to watch on Netflix. I said, "Are you friggin' kidding me? There's a butt load on there! There's so much on there I can't decide what to watch. I end up watching nothing." As they say, "A confused mind makes no decisions."

She just rolled her eyes and walked away. We were in apparent disagreement as to what was "something to watch" on Netflix. We have too much stuff!

When I was a kid, I would complain that there was nothing on TV. This was 1986, and there really was NOTHING on— except for The Cosby Show and The Brady Bunch reruns. Today, I can't imagine ever uttering those words. There are so many channels on streaming; it's ridiculous. I only watch two channels, and I just recently added a third. I can't handle any more than that. I can't keep track of what I was watching the night before!

Here's a complaint that's been coming out of my mouth recently. Actually, two complaints:

On Netflix and/or Amazon Prime...

1. They rearrange the order of the movies, so I can't keep track of what I watched recently.
2. They change the cover image of the movie, so I can't recall what I was watching.

Of course, this will all be irrelevant in years to come. However, I just wanted to point out that I still complain about a lot of shit. I'm getting better. When I do complain, I just say to myself, "Whatever. Move on. It's not worth getting upset over. Let's just enjoy...[whatever I can think of at that moment.]"

Do you want to know what one of my favorite movies is? It's *Pollyanna*. People love to bash this movie or make disparaging references such as, "We should live in a better world, but not in a Pollyanna-ish type world." As if that were a bad thing.

If you're not familiar with the movie *Pollyanna*, here is a quick synopsis:

Pollyanna had a game she would play that would make her feel better whenever she was dissatisfied with anything. She loved this little game so much that she would tell everyone about it. She managed to annoy quite a few people with her little game.

The game was called The Glad Game. If you were ever upset about anything, you would play The Glad Game. The game went like this. Whenever you were upset, you would think of something to be glad about.

In one example in the movie, she was given a pair of crutches as a Christmas charity gift from the local mission. She really wanted a doll. Instead of being upset, she turned it around and decided to be glad that she didn't *need* the crutches. Get it?

A lot of people don't get it and think it's stupid. I think we don't appreciate all that we have. And the more that we get, the more that we complain. This complaining has a severe effect on our health—especially the heart. Now, when I complain, I notice it in my heart. It was always there, but now I know why it was there. It was from all that complaining.

Also, when you complain, you keep good things from coming to you. Ever since I stopped complaining, I noticed all sorts of good fortune come my way.

History

I love history. It gives me perspective. When it snows, I'm thankful that I have a shovel. I am grateful I can heat my car. I am thankful I can heat my home. But not everyone has this perspective.

Have you ever wondered why the people of the past wore so much clothing? Maybe because they didn't have central heat. They were cold all the time. I know people today who hang out inside their homes in February with only a t-shirt and shorts. What a luxury!

I see children waiting at the bus stops in just shorts. That bus must be nicely heated—as well as the school. They didn't have that 100 years ago. But I'm sure kids today would complain that the soda machine ran out of Coke. To be fair, I'm not just pointing out the kids of today. What I mean is kids of modern times. When I was a kid, we also complained about soda and other meaningless stuff.

We need to look at history and how they lived to really appreciate our lives now. When we complain about things, we don't truly appreciate our lives now. That's a shame. That is one thing that my heart palpitations opened my eyes to. I learned that I wasn't enjoying my life. I only have one life, so I better start appreciating it. Do you know why? Because no one else will!

Appreciate the small things

Whenever you complain about something, think about the good things about it. For instance, the other day, I was listening to my iPod Shuffle at the gym while I was working out. As usual, my earbuds got all tangled up. I started to complain about how they got all tangled up all the time.

In trying to curb my complaining, I started to think about all the good things about my iPod. I realized what a luxury it was to have such a small device that could hold so much music. Years ago, I had to bring a portable tape player (Walkman style) or a portable CD player to the gym. These were big, bulky, heavy, and clumsy. And they could only hold 45 mins of music—only twelve songs!

So, what if my iPod earbuds got tangled up? I had hundreds of songs to listen to! What was I complaining about? This iPod was so small, I hardly noticed I even had it. At this realization, I stopped complaining, and I started appreciating.

I appreciated that Steve Jobs and Apple created such an excellent device where I could listen to my favorite music so easily. This changed for me. I was able to enjoy my workout a lot more.

Heart palp cure action plan

When you're in a place that seems to be overcrowded, thank your lucky stars that you don't live in China, where they have four times the population as the US in the same amount of space.

When your Starbucks coffee is taking too long to make, thank your lucky stars that you don't live in the 1950s where Rosy, the counter lady, would serve bland coffee in a four-ounce coffee cup.

When you must commute to work in heavy traffic, thank your lucky stars you don't have to work in a coal mine where your life is in danger every single day.

When you get broccoli instead of curly fries, thank your lucky stars that you get something to eat. Instead, you could be starving in some war-torn country.

I'm not perfect, but I'm getting better. I learn to appreciate things more. This simple act has helped me reduce my heart palpitations.

But let's be very clear: Don't give up complaining because it makes you a good person. Give up complaining because it's good for your health. I'm a huge believer in doing things for selfish reasons. Sometimes doing something for the good of all isn't enough of a motivator to do the right thing.

When it comes to your heart health, giving up complaining is really, really good for your heart. I promise you that.

And I'm not just talking about complaining at the watercooler or to the person in line at Disney World. I'm talking about every moment you have with yourself, every moment you have an opportunity to complain, and every moment something doesn't go your way.

These are the times where keeping your complaining to a minimum will have amazing effects on your heart. It's these internal—unresolvable—complaints that will wreak havoc on your heart.

It's entirely all right to complain to the counter person if you got a cold cheeseburger when it should have been hot. This kind of complaining will bring about change. You might get your grievance be resolved.

What's not okay is eating the cold cheeseburger and then complaining about it on the drive home and then complaining some more for the next ten years. I'm sure we all have these stories.

The way life is

I had been repeating a story about getting the wrong sandwich for years. No one seemed all that sympathetic. I guess they have their own "wrong sandwich" story, but somehow it wasn't worth bitchin' about. It took me a long time to get that message.

But when I did, the whole world opened for me. Okay, maybe not the entire world, but it was a massive load off my shoulder. I made a concerted effort to stop complaining about all the wrongs I had when I was a kid. I stopped complaining about my parents—who've been deceased for many years now. I stopped complaining about annoying relatives—whom I never see.

Sometimes, that's just the way life is.

Whenever I watch safari documentaries, I often imagine this scenario:

The antelope are grazing in the grassland, and they spot a few lions in the area…

"Oh, shit. Here come those murderous lions again. Why must they come to kill us and eat us? Why can't they just eat grass like the rest of us? What's wrong with eating grass? It's delicious. Look, we're all eating grass and enjoying it. We like it. The zebras like it. What's the big deal about eating this delicious and nutritious grass? Why do those murderous lions have to come over here and take a big chunk out of us and then devour us? Why? Fuck this shit! SOMEONE should do something about this. It's NOT fair! Is anyone with me on this? Anyone? Anyone?"

Those antelope can complain all day long about the lions, but it won't change a thing. Now, of course, if they passed some laws, then something may change. But just sitting around and bitchin' about the way things are won't change a thing.

Before complaining, get the whole picture

Many years ago, I was in Spain on a school trip. On one particular day, our tour bus dropped us off at some deserted town. Ever seen *The Good, the Bad, and the Ugly* starring Clint Eastwood? It was that kind of deserty type place. A few tumbleweeds here and there. We were supposed to eat in some tourist trap food court. My friends and I decided to walk down the street to some local eatery. We wanted to get away from our group. They were annoying us too much.

We went into a local eatery that served sandwiches and soda. I asked for a jamón and queso, which is ham and cheese in Spanish. Those were the only words I knew how to say.

Guess what I got when I got my sandwich?

I got ham.

And cheese.

Slapped between two slices of bread—a French roll, to be exact.

That was it!

No lettuce. No tomato. No mayo. No mustard. No pickles. No onion. Nothing else!

I. Was. Pissed.

I sat there at my table, sulking for a few minutes. I was looking at this sandwich. I raised the top of the French roll to reveal the ham. The ham was about half an inch thick. I was expecting several thin slices of ham. But no. I got ONE thick slice.

Then I picked up the ham and looked at the cheese beneath. It, too, was a half an inch thick. I was also expecting several much thinner slices of cheese.

And after I lifted the cheese, there was the lonely bottom half of the French roll. That's it. Just four items:

1. Top of the roll
2. ONE slice of ham
3. ONE slice of cheese
4. Bottom of the roll.

That was it!

I'm NOT kidding!

I pushed the plate away. How am I going to eat this dreadful sandwich? Look how thick that ham is! And where's the mayo? And where's the mustard? And the lettuce and the sliced tomatoes? I was pissed.

The only reason I didn't get up and complain is that I didn't know conversational Spanish. All I knew was ham (jamón), cheese (queso), and "Dónde está el baño?" (Where's the bathroom?). That was pretty much it.

So, going up to the counter person and complaining would have been useless. At least here in America at the Dunkin' Donuts, I have a shot at getting through to someone. "My coffee is TOO hot—muy caliente! Capiche?"

I didn't get up to leave the restaurant because my friends were enjoying their sandwiches. I think they got cheeseburgers (smart choice).

Also, I was starving, and I didn't want to go back to the tourist trap food court.

So, I stayed and sulked. Finally, after bitchin' about it for a bit, I started eating my ham and cheese sandwich (with no mayo, no mustard, no lettuce, and no tomato). I took one bite. And then another. It had an exciting flavor. The whole sandwich seemed very dry. The ham was dry. The bread was dry. The cheese was dry.

Guess what?

It was THE BEST sandwich I've had in my entire life! Seriously, I can never stop talking about this sandwich. I tell everyone about this sandwich. I've not had a better sandwich since, and I've had some pretty good sandwiches over the years. But just those three ingredients somehow made for a most enjoyable and memorable experience for me.

So now, I am a little more careful about how I judge things. Also, I learned to thoroughly investigate things (like eating a sandwich) before going on a tirade.

I talk about that sandwich so much my wife gets upset every time I bring it up.

"Austin, you're not talking about that sandwich you had in Spain again?"

"Yes. Why not? It was a good sandwich."

"But we've heard about it a million times."

"That's because it was a good sandwich."

"But you insert that story into every conversation. 'What's the best vacation you ever had, Austin?' 'Oh, I had this awesome sandwich in Spain.' 'What's your favorite food?' 'Ham and cheese sandwiches from Spain.' 'Where would you like to go on your next vacation?' 'Spain. They have the best ham and cheese sandwiches' and on and on."

"That's not true."

"Yes, it is. The other day we were talking about Christmas decorations, and somehow you brought up that godforsaken ham and cheese sandwich from Spain."

"First of all, it was not a godforsaken sandwich. God did not forsake anything—me or the sandwich. Secondly, your grandmother was asking about bringing a spiral ham for the Christmas Eve dinner. She brought up ham, so I figured I would relate to her on a ham level. Therefore, the story about my most wonderful ham and cheese sandwich was highly relevant."

"Well, you talk about it way too much."

"No, I don't."

"Yeah, you do. You'll probably write about your sandwich in a book or something."

"No, I won't."

And that conversation goes on almost every three to four months. It's not my fault I learned to appreciate the good things in life. If I happen to like a good ham and cheese sandwich, so be it. Who doesn't love a good ham and cheese sandwich?

The sad, unfortunate part of this story is that I never really learned to appreciate other things in my life. Somehow the ham and cheese sandwich moral lesson never cemented into my psyche. I spent the next twenty years complaining about all sorts of things. Cold soup, smelly gym socks, toe cheese, crazy taxi drivers, lazy waiters, bad haircuts, bad weather on vacations, good weather on "lazy days," red lights, green lights when I'm trying to read a map/book/note, etc., popcorn prices at the movie theater, bad BO, smelly dogs, cats with attitudes, etc., etc.

And the list just goes on. It wasn't until I had massive episodes with my heart palpitations that I started to see the error of my ways. It took a while, but I slowly crawled out of the quicksand. I owe a lot of my success with overcoming heart palpitations to not complaining about all the stuff I used to complain about.

Conclusion

The reality of the matter is that I could write a book of biblical proportions (meaning really long) about what complaining does to your psyche and eventually to your heart. But I won't. We have other areas to cover.

You must keep your complaining to a minimum. You must be aware of what you are complaining about. Whenever you see yourself complaining, compare your situation to someone else's life. You will soon see that whatever you are complaining about is not worth complaining about.

Key takeaways

- Complaining will affect your heart
- Stop complaining will reduce your heart palpitations
- Complaining is overrated
- When complaining, put yourself in someone else's shoes
- Fully evaluate your situation before complaining about your sandwich

-6-

What's Wrong with Being Right All the Time?

I know people who always try to be right all the time. Your efforts to be right all the time will hamper your efforts to get better. And I do mean hamper. No kidding! Lots of hamper.

When you try to be right all the time, you are resisting other people's information. You are resisting. As mentioned before, what you resist persists.

Arguing

When you argue with people, you are adamant that you are right. In many cases, you are not. Most people claim their point without a lot of information to go on. They just stick their heels into the ground and argue.

The problem with arguing is that if you lose the argument, you will feel defeated. You didn't get your way. If you win the argument, you got your way. However, you may feel guilty about it subconsciously.

Suppose you and your spouse argued about where you should take the family on your next vacation. You wanted to go skiing in Colorado, but your spouse wanted a Caribbean vacation. You win the argument. Was it really a win if your spouse is not having a good time skiing in Colorado?

Subconsciously, you will feel this stress. Consciously, your ego is happy that you won the argument. You are victorious. You get to do what you wanted to do. But deep down, there is a sense of guilt. It's that sense of guilt that causes the stress and anxiety that is wreaking havoc on your heart. Sometimes, it's not worth standing your ground if you ultimately are not going to feel good about it.

Try to see things from their perspective

When it comes to arguing, let it go. Give in or try to find a middle ground. Try to see things from the other person's point of view. I came to this realization as I got older. During my younger years, I would also complain and sulk about how shitty my parents were. When I got to their age (in my late forties), I realized that they did the best they could with what they had to work with. I was able to see the whole situation from their point of view.

Every time I'm able to see a situation from someone else's point of view, it immediately releases the tension inside of me. I don't necessarily have to give in to my side of the argument. However, putting myself in their shoes allows me to ease my tensions and open my eyes to the bigger picture.

This has been an enormous help in terms of my heart health. As I began to give in and take my heels out of the ground, I noticed that my heart palpitations slowly subsided. This really works.

Try this little experiment: The next time you are in an argument with someone, take a step back and look at the situation from their point of view. You'll be surprised by what you see. And you will be equally surprised by how much better you feel. Now, this doesn't mean you have to fold and rollover. You may very well be right with your side of the argument. You just need to see things from their perspective.

We carry so much in our hearts. There is a lot of science behind this. I'm not a doctor or a scientist, so I will not go into this. However, there is a huge connection between our subconscious mind and our hearts.

When I stopped arguing with people and always trying to get my way, I could feel my heart getting better. My heart feels great now, and I am nearly free of all the heart palpitations I suffered for years. I know if I went back to my old ways and started arguing every little point, my heart palpitations would start to creep in.

Correcting people

My friend does this all the time. She's always correcting people, and she's always correcting me. She can't seem to let things go.

She once told me of an incident where she couldn't get people to listen to her. She was out with a few friends, and those friends were in the company of a few of their friends. These friends of friends were talking about their forthcoming trip to England. They were discussing how they needed to exchange their American dollars for European Euros.

My friend rightly pointed out that England doesn't use Euros. They use Pounds. They didn't believe her, and the two parties argued about it for about twenty minutes. (By the way, this was in 2006, just before iPhone and instant access to all the info you could ever want in the palm of your hands).

As a result, my friend's friends stopped being friends with her. When my friend told me this story, I just wanted to say to her that she must stop trying to be right all the time. However, I'm a good and faithful friend, so I kept my mouth shut.

However, I am going to tell you to stop correcting people. What does it accomplish to fix people? Who cares if they are wrong and walk around being ignorant?

Now, there is a fine line between nicely correcting someone who is doing something clearly wrong—such as a haircut. But if it turns into an argument (like the incident mentioned above), let it go.

Your heart will thank you.

Let it go

A good book to read for letting things go is called *Letting Go* by David Dawkins. This book will show you what is going on inside you when you feel angry, frustrated, and about twenty other negative emotions. Once you learn about what's going inside you, you can let things go.

This is one of the overreaching things that I learned during my journey to curing my agonizing heart palpitations. I had to learn to let things go. Often when I would get mad at something, I would not express my anger. I would keep it bottled up.

Eventually, this anger must come out somehow, and it must manifest itself someway. The way things manifested for me was through my heart palpitations. When I was able to suppress my heart palpitations with supplements like Magnesium and Hawthorn berries, my body would express my anger through body aches and pains.

Many of these aches and pains were in my chest area. This naturally scared the hell out of me. While I didn't have heart palpitations, I had sharp pains across my chest. I thought maybe I was having a heart attack. Later, I learned that these pains were rather benign.

Through these aches and pains, I discovered how much my mind played a role in my heart palpitations.

I know it plays a role in everyone else's problem. People want to blame a physical illness, and they want to get some medicine from a doctor. They want to tell the world that they have a faulty valve or something.

What they don't want to do is admit that they have a nasty disposition, or they are just an angry person. This is not a very flattering thing to realize about oneself. It's easier to say and to admit that you have a floppy heart valve, or you lack magnesium. Much easier than to say that you are angry at the world and are frustrated as hell.

However, those in denial are the ones who are more likely to have a nasty disposition. Not recognizing what's going on inside only keeps you from getting better. Staying in denial will only enhance your anger and frustration. This of course must manifest itself in some physical way. For us, it's the feeling that our hearts are going to explode, and we are going to drop dead.

It's nasty

I had a nasty disposition (and sometimes I still do), but I didn't want to admit it. I didn't want to admit it all. I thought my solution to my dreadful heart palpitations was through diet, exercise, and supplements. Those helped—in a placebo kind of way—but it wasn't until I addressed my mind and how I viewed the world did I find a real, long-lasting cure for my heart palpitations.

One of the bad habits I had was trying to be right all the time. I wouldn't let myself be wrong about anything. Once I let things go, I felt the tension melt away. The pressure went away in my shoulders and back.

> *"Would I rather be right, or would I rather be kind?"*
> —Wayne Dyer

Several years ago, a friend of mine came to me with a business proposition. He wanted me to help him build a website for selling some goods. To be honest, I don't know what it was that he wanted to sell, but at the time it didn't sound like the most promising thing.

Since I knew a lot about web design and online marketing, he came to me with his proposition. Being a web designer and an online marketer, I hear these proposals all the time. Someone will come to me with a great idea, and they want me to do all the work. They think that since they came up with the idea, they should get equal share while I do all the work. That's not how these things work. However, that's a story for another book.

Anyway, since this was the billionth time that I had heard about one of these online business propositions, I really wasn't in the mood to give this much thought. For everything my friend said to me, I turned it around and told him how wrong he was. It went like this:

Friend: "We could set up a website and sell these to everyone."

Me: "Everyone? What do you mean everyone? You mean militants in sub-Saharan Africa and church ladies alike? You mean that kind of everyone?"

Friend: "No, I mean like lots of people. The people who need this."

Me: "Do they really need this? What do people need, anyway? We have everything we need. We have food, shelter, and clothes on our backs. Who needs what you're offering?"

Friend: "You're not seeing the big picture here."

Me: "Yes, I am. It's not that easy to whip up a website and start selling shit. You don't know what you're talking about."

Friend: "Why are you attacking me?"

Me: "I'm not attacking you. I'm just telling you… that you don't just wake up one day, create a website, and think you will make a bunch of money."

Friend: "But people make money online all the time."

Me: "Yeah, and it's a lot of work. You're kidding yourself if you think it's easy!"

Friend: "There you go again. You're attacking me."

Me: "No, I'm not. I'm just trying to be real here. Setting up a website is hard. Getting people to your website is even harder. Getting people to buy anything is a monumental task. It's not that easy. There is a buttload of failed websites."

Well, that was the end of that argument—and the end of that friendship. I was right, and he was wrong. Was I really right? In my head, I was right. But who knows? I could be dead wrong. In either case, I could have handled the situation much better.

In fact, for many days, weeks, and years later, I kept hearing him saying, "You're attacking me." I *was* attacking him. I was getting in his face and letting him know how wrong he was about the ease of making money online. I had to be right (for whatever reason). In the end, it wasn't worth it to be haunted by those words all these years later.

Ultimately, I realized how trying to be right all the time had a severe effect on my health—especially my heart. As I started to let things go and let things be, I began to lift my spirit and my heart health. It is quite amazing how your disposition can affect your heart—among other organs in your body.

Conclusion

You could go around life and try to prove how right you are. Your ego will reward you for such ventures. However, it is your subconscious mind that will be taking notice. You will heighten your anxiety and perpetuate your heart palpitations because your subconscious knows. Do you really want that?

Key takeaways

- Try to see things from other people's view
- Let things go
- Your ego will be rewarded for being right, but your subconscious will suffer

-7-

Mind Your Business and Calm Your Heart

With the advent of social media and the childish news coverage, it seems like no one can mind their own business. This is very damaging to all—especially to people who have some form of anxiety or suffer from heart palpitations.

You are your best keeper

When you are minding someone else's business, you are NOT minding your own business. Who is going to look after your life as well as you?

No one.

That's right. You are the only one who will be 100% invested in how your life turns out. No one else. So, minding someone else's business is not putting 100% of your attention onto yourself.

Sadly, we are a society that is in everyone's business. We have the P.C. police, we have HOAs, we have comments on blog posts, we have Facebook feeds, etc. Everyone seems to be giving their opinion about someone or something. It's okay to have an idea and to express it.

The problem comes when that's all you seem to do with your days. When you are paying attention to other people and what they are doing, you are paying less attention to what you are doing. This creates a dissonance in your mind and in your heart.

It's very unsettling to your mind. When your mind is unsettled, your heart will react. I know this for sure. I started getting my heart palpitations in earnest when I was starting my own freelance business. Instead of focusing on what I was doing, I was spending all my time on what everyone else was doing.

I even participated in the social media conversation—something I deeply regret today. I know people don't like to hear it, and I know that people need their social media. But you must ask yourself at what cost. Is having those unbearable heart palpitations worth it? Is it fun to have your heart beat so fast and erratically that it feels like it's going blast out of your chest and flop onto the floor? No to me!

Who cares?

You must ask yourself, "Why do I care?"

Often, I ask my friends and family members why they care. Seriously, why do they care so much about what other people are doing? Whenever they are talking about someone, I ask them why they care. Rarely do they come up with a good answer. They often tell me that they just don't know.

Why do you care?

Why do you care what other people are doing? Is it really that important what other people are doing or even thinking? If you think about it, it's rather absurd. Do you think the highly successful people in the world have a lot of time worrying about what other people are doing? No. They are too busy minding their own business and being successful.

Global problem

The amount of meddling we do in other countries has had many unforeseen issues. We tried to bring food to Ethiopia and Somalia. Are they any better off?

We tried to bring democracy to many other countries. Are they any better off? Who knows? Maybe those countries would be better off without democracy.

What does this have to do with you and your heart issues? Again, this is the media sucking you in and forcing you to care about things you don't need to care about.

Whenever there is some oddball news story, everyone feels a need to weigh in. A while back there was a news story where a family faked a balloon ride, and their young child accidentally got stuck in a homemade balloon. Everyone had an opinion on the matter. Why? Who cares? Who really gives a shit?

USA Today online has an article titled: *"5 years later: 'Balloon Boy,' family still search for fame."*

So what?

There's just too much garbage floating through the airwaves and into your brain. Mind your own business. Your heart will thank you for it.

This is the type of shit that chips away a little more of your mind. Think about all these things I am talking about in this book, chipping away at your psyche. You don't notice it at first, but over time, it will catch up to you. And I know it is catching up to you because you have heart palpitations.

When your mind and your heart are out of coherence, your heart will act up.

Foreign wars

The United States has engaged in many foreign wars because we aren't able to mind our own business. No one really knows if we would have been better off if we stayed out of the Middle East. The jury may still be out on that.

Regardless of whether the U.S. government is sending troops to a foreign land to fight a war or not, you should have no opinion on the matter. Don't make the United States government's opinion your opinion. Be independent.

As I've often said, this is your life. You only get one. How do you want to live it? Your heart palpitations are a symptom that something is seriously wrong with your unconscious mind. Minding your own business is an excellent way to get yourself on the right path.

A lot of people have argued with me on this. They tell me that we should care and be mindful of world politics. I then ask them, "Do you suffer from distressful heart palpitations that keep you up at night?"

If their answer is, "No," I then say, "Okay, then never mind. Keep minding everyone's business."

If the answer is, "Yes," I then say, "Are you crazy? Do you really like stressing about your erratically thumping heart? Do you really enjoy to feeling like you are going to die every few minutes? Is that fun? No? Then stop staying abreast of our global politics and minding other people's business. They don't give a shit about you."

You will thank me later when you adopt this new attitude toward world affairs. They don't care about you. Don't give them the attention.

P.C. Culture

We now have the thought police. We have the P.C. (politically correct) police telling us what to say, how to say it, when to say it, and who to say it to. The P.C. police will invent things for people to be upset about.

You are punished not for the things that you say but for the things you think. Don't get caught up in this. Don't participate in this drama. Keep minding your own business, and you will be on your way to a happy heart.

HOAs

Homeowners Associations are the ultimate vehicle for minding someone else's business. They cannot NOT mind someone's business. That's what they are all about. Their motto should be: *HOAs—Minding Your Business Every Step of the Way.*

When you mind someone else's business, you are like a mini-HOA. Have you heard of these HOAs? They are like mini totalitarian dictatorships. All they do is mind someone else's business.

You must let things go. This is the essence of healing your heart. When you are minding other people's business, you are thinking outwardly, not inwardly. The path to healing your heart is to think inwardly. We'll discuss more about that later.

You only have one life.

I often say that you have only one life to live. How do you want to live it? Do you want to live it meddling in other people's business? Or do you want to have complete command of your own business?

Michael Crichton (author of Jurassic Park and other novels) said this on a news broadcast:

> "I'm interested in the extent to which people... What is it that makes people want to tell other people how to behave...Some people feel they really know how everybody ought to be... I have my hands full just taking care of myself....I'm interested in what psychologically make somebody have that confidence, and the other part of that is that I think there is a deep and secret human impulse to live in a totalitarian state."

This is very profound, and Crichton is onto something. Many people do secretly want to live in a totalitarian state. It's frightening. When you mind other people's business, you are participating in a totalitarian state in which everyone is being told what to do by someone else.

Is this how you want to live? Or do you want to live free? Do you want to have freedom of choice of what to say, what to do, and how to live? Remember, the world is a giant mirror reflecting upon you what you put out.

When I say these things in Facebook groups for anxiety and heart palpitations, people think I'm off my rocker. I need to remind them that I suffered from terrible heart palpitations for four years, and then I cured myself of all symptoms within six months. I'm not off my rocker. I'm very much on my rocker and enjoying life like I never have before.

The way I found my everlasting cure was to take stock in the way I was behaving. It was very toxic. Overtime, after I stopped participating in toxic behavior, I was able to hear my inner voice and find a real solution to my debilitating heart palpations.

Do you really want to go to bed scared out of your mind that your heart will thump around all night? Do you want to have another day where you wonder if you will have another massive SVT episode—the kind where you think you will drop dead? Do you really want to spend another $2,500 for an ambulance and a hospital stay for something you could have easily resolved if you only heeded this advice and found your inner voice?

Inner guidance

One reason why people don't mind their own business is that they are disconnected from their own Truth. They can no longer hear their inner guidance. They no longer have direction, so they need to tell other people what to do and how to do it. This is very unhealthy. You must listen to your inner guidance.

Minding someone else's business might be your way of bringing some excitement or conflict to an otherwise dull existence. This is where you need to occupy yourself with constructive activities. You need things that positively stimulate your mind.

An idle mind will only conjure up anxious thoughts. I know this happened to me. When I was sitting around not doing much, I thought about my heart palpitations. It wasn't until I got myself involved in activities and made a concerted effort to mind my own business and reduce my anxious thoughts.

People will often poke their nose in other people's affairs because they know that these other people have better lives going on. This creates inner turmoil inside you. Ultimately, this will manifest into heart palpitations.

Life purpose

Not minding your own business often means you don't have a life purpose. If there is one thing that I learned on my journey to be cured of my god-awful heart palpitations is that I didn't have a life purpose. I was just flailing along, waiting for something to happen to my life.

Guess what?

When something did happen, it would make me anxious. When you sit around waiting for something to happen, you won't be prepared for when it happens. Have you ever heard the expression "A good defense is a good offense."? Well, it's true if you want to keep calm and reduce your heart palpitations.

If you have a life purpose and you are moving forward with your life and are making things happen, you will have a good offense. When something unexpected happens, you will be very well prepared. It won't throw you off and make you anxious.

When you have your life's purpose, you won't be interested in other people's lives. If you are feeling a need to be in other people's business, you may be feeling unworthy. This feeling can manifest itself into heart palpitations.

I see this in the Facebook communities often. There are a lot of people who feel unworthy and want sympathy. However, they also dole out unsolicited advice that is usually wrong!

I know that this happened to me. I felt like I needed to be in everyone's business. I felt very unworthy. I was unemployed and not really having any real direction in life. I started minding other people's business. I would comment on what the neighbors were doing.

They watered their lawn too much—and their dog too little. Their Christmas décor looked drab and cheap—like it was purchased at Walmart.

One day, I looked at my neighbor's back yard from my second-floor office window. It was always filled with trash. Since it was behind a wooden fence, no one else could see it except for me from my second-floor window.

One day instead of getting mad about it, I just said, "I have really great neighbors." I meant it, too!

Guess what happened?

Two days later, my neighbor cleaned out all the junk in his backyard. I no longer saw the junk pile from my second-floor window. The Universe listened and delivered.

When you have a life purpose, you won't have time to meddle in other people's business, and you won't have a desire to meddle in other people's business. This will result in a calm mind and healthy heart.

Try to see things from their point of view

Very often, we are guilty of the very things of which we judge others. When we are minding other people's business, we are essentially judging them. We are so accustomed to doing this that we never really look at ourselves in the mirror.

Consciously, we think we know better and that we are doing a good thing. But deep down, our subconscious knows the truth. Our subconscious doesn't lie. When you feel a dissonance, it's your subconscious at work.

Our ego-mind or conscious mind can mask these feelings, but our subconscious cannot. It will manifest itself in some way. For some people, they get skin problems or hair problems. Some people may get sick a lot. By the way, I have never fallen ill since I cured myself of my heart palpitations. I can say that and *not* knock on wood. Some people develop much more severe diseases.

This is our subconscious at work. When we mind other people's business, our subconscious knows that we are not paying enough attention to ourselves. Our mind, body, and soul will react. And for those reading this book, this means our hearts. Our hearts go haywire. They beat erratically, making our lives miserable. We need to clean things up.

If everyone minded their own business, the world would be a much better place. Think about all the misery and suffering that is going on. It's because people cannot mind their own damn business.

Most people think they are doing good by sticking their nose in some else's business. They are not.

Case in point. Charities. Charities are known for doing good things for people in need. However, there are some consequences of all this giving. Some people are hurt by it. Much of our used clothing gets dumped onto the shores of African countries. This puts local merchants out of business. Why should a local citizen buy a t-shirt from a local merchant when he can get a Nike t-shirt for free? This kind of minding-someone-else's-business charity hurts people on a massive scale.

If it's hard to imagine how this is a bad thing, just look at how China dumped a lot of cheap products into the U.S. and other western countries. It was a disaster.

What happened? A lot of our manufacturing went out of business. They couldn't compete. Many of our businesses went overseas. Most of our medicines are manufactured in China. Is that really what you want?

Are you not that important?

When you don't mind your business, you are telling yourself that you are not worthy, and you are not important. You are telling yourself that someone else is more important than you. Not minding your own business is negative self-talk in disguise.

Once you stop minding other people's business, you will feel tremendous relief. Just like any other bad habit, you will be out of your comfort zone, but soon you will feel much better. And your heart will thank you, too.

> *"The highest form of ignorance is when you reject something you don't know anything about."*
> —Wayne Dyer

When you stick your nose into other people's business, you often look foolish. I know this happened to me in more ways than I'd like to think about.

Conclusion

To stay on the path of a complete cure of your heart palpitations, the first step is to mind your own business as much as possible. Unfortunately, social media and the childish news makes it extremely hard to mind your own business. However, it is possible, so at least give it a try.

I know from personal experience this works. I had debilitating heart palpitations for over four years. I was suffering so much that I just wanted to jump off a bridge. I couldn't figure out how to resolve my problem.

It wasn't until I realized that my mind was toxic. Part of that toxicity was sticking my nose and my thoughts into other people's lives. I was not focused on my life. I wasn't focused on my mind, body, and spirit. Now, I am. And I feel so much better. My heart is calm, and overall, I have a general feeling of joy.

Key takeaways

- Minding your own business will help heal your heart
- Think inward instead of outward
- Try to see things from someone else's perspective
- Minding other people's business can be harmful to others

-8-

When You Stop Doing This, You Will Find Great Relief

Stop watching the news. That is about as straight and simple as it gets. You must ask yourself, "What has the news done for me lately?"

First, let's start with how the news makes money.

As you know, the news makes their money through advertising. Advertisers pay based on how many eyeballs they think will see their ads, which is based on how many total people tune into the news. It's that simple. The more people watching the news, the more people will view the advertising. The news charges based on how many people are watching.

What is the objective of the news?

Is the news main objective to inform the public about current events?

No!

The sole objective of the news is to get you to watch for as long as possible. That is the objective. Don't be mistaken. The news is not there to inform you. If informing you makes them money, they will inform you. If informing you doesn't make them money, they won't inform you. They will do something else. It's that simple.

The news is a money-making enterprise. They are not your friends, and they are not good-will ambassadors. They are not the rulers of your life. They are there just to make money. If they didn't make money, they would go do something else.

Now that we know that the news is, let's explore why and how they can make a ton of money. After all, some of those news anchors make millions and millions of dollars a year. To do what? Read off a teleprompter. Sean Hannity of Fox News makes nearly eight million dollars a year. The news is big money!

How do they do it?

They keep you tuned in by instilling fear. Fear is a primal instinct. It works in times of danger. Because of the fear of being harmed, people will do anything NOT to be hurt. This is a fundamental physiological instinct.

You don't want to be harmed. You will do anything you can to *not* be hurt. There are exceptions to this rule, such as participating in extreme sports, doing crazy stunts, devotion to a job, etc. However, you are more likely to seek out a life where you avoid harm.

What's the best way to avoid great harm or death?

Be informed.

The more informed you are about what causes harm or death, the more likely you are to avoid injury and death. This is why babies have such a hard time navigating the world. They haven't learned anything. They have no idea what's going to harm them or kill them.

They don't know that sticking their finger in a light socket is going to kill them. This is what the growing up process is all about. It's about learning all the stuff that's gonna kill you. You learn this from your family, your friends, your school, and the media.

Some people have crazy, overzealous parents (I did), or mischievous friends. They sometimes scare you for no real reason. However, for the most part, they will impart some cautionary tale that will help you stay safe.

If you have a crazy mother as I did, everything you did would cost them (i.e., my parents) their house.

This was a constant refrain from my mother:

> "You found nude photos of your art teacher? They're gonna sue us and take the house!"

> "You were smoking pot in the boy's bathroom? They're gonna take the house!"

> "You ran away from a school trip? They're gonna take the house!"

> "You got suspended from school? They're gonna take the house!"

"You stole a Robert Plant album from Caldor®? They're gonna take the house!"

Yes, I did all those things, and no one ever took the house. However, that negativity carried with me all through my adult life.

And of course, I have my wife:

"You're eating that mayonnaise that's been sitting out all day? You're gonna get sick!"

"You're gonna eat that hotdog that rolled underneath the toilet? You're gonna get sick!"

"You're taking Advil after drinking three vodka-tonics? You're gonna die!"

"You're gonna take three times the recommended amount of... [pretty much every medication or vitamin I've ever consumed]? You're gonna die!

"You climbed into the living room window from our fourth-floor balcony? You could have fallen four floors and died!"

Yeah, yeah, whatever.

At any rate, we get a lot of negativity from a lot of well-meaning people. But make no mistake. The news is NOT a well-meaning friend. The news is there to make money. That's it.

You need to understand this. When I tell my friends that I don't watch the news, they think I'm crazy and often ask, "How do you stay informed?" I'll answer that shortly, but it cannot be stressed enough that the news is not your friend, and they are not there to inform you.

When you watch the news, you must ask yourself how relevant to your life is what they are saying. Below is an example of what set me off to stop watching the news.

Back in 2005, I was watching the local evening news. A report came on and said, "Eight people are dead as a result of a bus crash in [some remote Chinese province], China. A freak snowstorm covered the city. The bus was on a mountain road. Thirty-two people were injured, and eight people died. Up next, Dolly Parton pays a visit to Dollywood."

After watching that, I said, "What the hell was that all about? How is that news? What does a bus crash killing eight people in some remote province in China have anything to do with my life?"

This is what the news is today. Just a bunch of freak accidents to keep you tuned in. Now with scrolling tickers on the bottom of your screen, the stories are even more incomplete. They lack context. The news is not your friend, and they instill fear to make money. That's it. Don't be fooled by the guise of "informing the public."

On a national level, the news likes to cause division because that's what keeps people tuned in. The past election between Hillary Clinton and Donald Trump caused derision solely because of the media, and the news wanted it that way. You can say what you want about each candidate, but there is no denying that the news stirred the pot. A lot!

This book isn't about taking sides about political debates. However, if you want to cure your heart palpitations, you must not participate in the news media circus. And that's precisely what it is. It just goes around and around. They will stir the pot however they can. They don't really solve any problems for anyone.

Realizing this was a big step in helping me get rid of my devasting heart palpitations forever. If I hadn't weaned myself off the news, I know I would still be suffering badly from erratic heart beats. I know I would be up all night worrying about when the big one will come. If I hadn't made this choice, I would still be suffering from SVTs, PACs, and PVCs. I would be a total wreck.

Stirring the pot

There was an incident that happened in Texas in 1999 that typifies how far the media will go to stir the pot. There was an explosion at a Texas hotel outside of Dallas. The blast happened near the hotel's swimming pool, where many guests were enjoying the pool and the summer weather.

Instead of describing the lunacy of what happened, I will give you the short narration of what transpired. This scene takes place between a reporter and the fire marshal outside of the hotel.

Reporter: "Where was the explosion?"

Fire Marshal: "Near the swimming pool."

Reporter: "Who planted the bomb?"

Fire Marshal: "There was no bomb. It was most likely a gas explosion."

Reporter: "What did he look like?"

Fire Marshal: "Who?"

Reporter: "The person who did this."

Fire Marshal: "No one did this. It looks like an accidental gas explosion."

Back to the news camera:

Reporter: "The fire marshal isn't quite sure who's behind this. They are looking for suspects now."

From the newsroom:

Anchorwoman: "Is this domestic terrorism or someone from the Middle East?"

Reporter: "We are not sure. We are trying to nail that down."

This went on for nearly four hours. I remember it clearly because all the networks covered it, preempting every TV show on every channel. I didn't have cable at the time, so I only had a few channels to choose from. I was pissed.

The news just repeated that scenario over and over again, trying to get the Fire Marshal to say something other than an innocent accident took place. The reporters would talk to any professional on the scene. It was either the Police Chief, Fire Marshal, FBI, terrorism expert, etc.

The news reporter would ask, "What happened?"

The professional would say, "It was a gas explosion. Several people got hurt and windows were blown out."

The news reporter would ask, "How many dead?"

The professional would say, "No one died. Some did get hurt from the glass. The explosion blew out some windows."

"Who did this?"

"No one. It was an accidental explosion."

"Are there any suspects?"

"No."

Back to the anchor desk:

Reporter: "They haven't located any suspects. They are unsure of how many people died from this event. They haven't ruled out terrorism."

On and on it went.

I spent four hours yelling at the TV.

> "Look, there was an accidental gas explosion near the pool! No one died. It was an accident, so NO suspects. No terrorism because there are NO suspects. Can we get back to *Friends*, for crying out loud!"

They kept trying to make it a terrorism issue. They latched onto the terrorism because the Oklahoma bombing happened just a few years before. (For those who are not aware. Oklahoma is the next state north of Texas. I just wanted to let you know so you don't have to whip out a map or Google. I need you to stay focused on this book. Yes, it's that important).

First to break the story

Take a moment and think about all the news stories in which the news personnel don't know anything about what they are reporting. Just like the example I gave you, every news channel tries to be the first to break a news story. They don't really care how wrong they are. They just want to be first. They follow the axiom: "Don't ask for permission. Just do it and apologize later." However, what they are really doing is instilling unnecessary fear upon the public.

People like you and me watch the news and become fearful of what's going to happen. Most people get stressed by the news; we all react in different ways. For people like you and me, we get these dreadful heart palpitations that make our lives a living hell. I'm so glad that's all behind me now. If it isn't for you, then please stop watching the news.

If the news is so bad, why are we so attracted to it?

The news prays upon one of our most primal instincts. That instinct is to protect ourselves from danger. Since we don't walk around with clubs and spears—and we live in the information age—we use information to protect ourselves from those unforeseen dangers.

When the news tells us about a plane crash, we want to know what type of plane, where it was taking off, was it pilot error, etc. The scenario might go something like this:

Commercial jet or private aircraft?

Commercial jet? I better listen up.

Private aircraft? It doesn't affect me. I don't travel in small planes.

Did it crash in the U.S. or some foreign land?

In this U.S.?

I better listen up. I live in the U.S. and fly all the time.

In Zimbabwe?

No big deal. I don't plan on going to Zimbabwe in my lifetime.

Pilot error or mechanical error?

Pilot error?

Next time I'm at the airport, I'll make sure my pilot isn't at the bar having cocktails.

Mechanical error?

The next I'm on the plane, and they say there is a delay because of mechanical problems, I'm getting off.

So, you run through all these scenarios in your head.

You watch the news report about the plane crash because you want to gather information to see how much it affects you. You are trying to protect yourself from a possible future event. This is the very definition of anxiety.

Therefore, when they report on a bus crash in a freak snowstorm in some remote province in China, it bothers me. Because it has no bearing on anyone's lives in the United States—except for a tiny, tiny, tiny group of people. These may be family members of someone living in that remote province of China or someone planning on taking a trip there. However, in my estimation, the percentage of people in this group would have to be 0.00001% of the total U.S. population. And that's being generous.

Let's look at this a little more closely to see how ridiculous these kinds of news stories are. There are 1.4 billion people in China. More precisely that's 1,386,000,000 people. The population of the United States is 327,200,000. That's roughly 327 million people. There were 8 deaths on that bus in China.

For argument's sake, let's say that each one of those people who died knows 1,000 people. That comes to 8,000 people who would be intimately affected by this sad news. Now, let's suppose for some strange and crazy reason all those 8,000 people happened to be relatives living in the United States.

So, let's divide 8,000 by 327 million to see what percentage of the United States population would be intimately affected by a bus crash in China. That number comes to 0.0024%. That's not 1% of our population that would be affected by this sad news about a bus crash in some remote province in China. It's not one-half percent. It's less than a half of a half of one percent. That's super tiny. Why the news story for so few people to be affected? Fear keeps you tuned in. Stop watching the news!

The news just wants to report death and destruction, no matter how remote it is or how little it affects our lives. They know they will get eyeballs. Because we are wired to protect ourselves, we use information to protect ourselves from future events.

Can you see how the news is manipulating you?

The news instills fear. And that's it. Knowing about all these news reports doesn't really lower your chances of surviving whatever you are trying to avoid.

Even if you watched every news report about plane crashes, you still have the same chances of dying in a car or a train crash. It's not going to help you to watch news stories about plane crashes.

The only thing it does is raise your anxiety. And your constant subconscious worrying is what is contributing to your heart palpitations. I know this all too well. When I stopped looking at every plane crash on the news, I felt so much better.

It's sad to see how the news instills fear in everything we do.

I was talking to a friend of mine recently. He had been unemployed for a few years and had gone back to school to get his master's degree. He was hoping this advanced degree would help him get a job. When I was speaking with him on this particular day, he was just three months from graduating. He told me he wanted to drop out. He was only three months from graduating from graduate school and wanted to drop out. What was going on?

As we were talking, he said this:

"It's gonna be hard to get a job. It's gonna be a lot harder than I thought. And even at the salary I'm seeking and my age. And now with Trump messing around with China and the trade wars…"

I had to stop listening. I paused a moment and let him ramble.

I then asked, "What does China have to do with you getting a job?"

"Well, with the economy and the trade wars."

"And do you think sitting there worrying about it is gonna help?"

"Well, it's just so bad."

"Who cares! You need to find a job. Do you think China is sitting there feeling bad for you? Do think that China is saying we better not do X, Y, and Z because Stan is at home worried about not getting a job. Hell, no!"

I was really pissed because my friend typified so many people in this country. I call them parrots because they watch the news and just repeat whatever was said on the news. When I have conversations with people, I can determine that they watch a lot of news because every word out of their mouth sounds like a news soundbite.

It was painfully evident that my friend Stan was obsessed with the news and how it was affecting his life. But only in his head.

China's trade war with the U.S. or the U.S.'s trade war with China has no bearing on whether my friend Stan gets a job. And Donald Trump and China don't give a flying shit about my friend Stan. He needs to look out for himself.

I told him to stop watching the news. In fact, I had told him many times before. Also, whenever we would go out and have a drink, he would bring up current events. My answer was usually, "I don't know. I don't watch the news." Or if I'm feeling very irritable, I will say, "I don't know, and I don't give a shit. And I'm pretty damn happy about that."

My friend is a perfect example of how a lot of people walk around like zombies. He was very depressed. But it was of his own making. His ability to get a job had no bearing on whether China and the U.S. are engaged in a trade war.

Yes, in the grand scheme of things, specific sectors of the economy will be hurt by a trade war. But worrying about it won't make it NOT happen. It will happen whether you sit and worry about it or not. There are forces bigger than you realize at work here.

The point I am trying to make is that planes will crash. A trade war will or will not happen. All these things will happen whether you sit around and worry about it or not. So, stop worrying about it. The best way to stop worrying about it is to stop participating in the news circus. They are a bunch of clowns who only disseminate bad news so they can make more money. It's about money, NOT informing the public.

How does this affect you?

Think about your heart.

You may not think you have anxiety, but if you have heart palpitations, there is an excellent chance it's all coming from your head—not some physical ailment. You need to fix your head.

The first place to start is to stop watching the news. Trust me, you won't miss anything. The news is all fake anyway. It always has been.

Politics

There is a straightforward way to exercise your frustration with the leaders of this country (America). It's called voting. It may not seem fair. It may not look clean. But it's the best system we have.

Nearly every American citizen has an opportunity to vote. Unfortunately, only a few people bother to vote. However, a much larger percentage exercise their frustrations on social media. And some braindead people go out and protest. For what? I have no idea.

It makes no sense to talk about your frustrations with the leaders of our country to your friends or coworkers. They are in no position to do anything. They voted just like you did. That's all that you can do.

Yes, you can write to your congressman or woman and complain to them. That you should do. But don't exercise your frustrations with those laymen who can't do anything about your frustrations.

It's a fruitless endeavor.

What's even a sadder situation is that fewer people are voting in local elections—where you have more control over who gets elected. Many state officials are elected on very slim margins—sometimes by only a few votes.

If you got your fat ass off the recliner and went out to vote in your local elections, you would have less to complain about. You would feel like you are doing something. You would lessen your anxiety—which in turn would reduce your heart palpitations.

In national elections, your vote has less effect; however, you should still vote. And once you vote, move on. Don't cry about it. That will accomplish nothing. You only have ONE life to live. Do you want to live a happy life? Or do you want to live a life where you're complaining about shit in which you have NO control over? The choice is yours. (Please make the right one).

Many years ago, I made that choice. I used to watch politics on TV. I watched the Sunday morning shows with David Brinkley and George Stephanopoulos. I got all riled up and cursed the world, and it got me nowhere. I was unemployed and unemployable. I was too angry. No one would hire me.

It wasn't until years later, where I made the connection of complaining about the world and my lack of success. I came to realize that watching politics was a significant source of my frustration and complaining.

Considering the success of CNN, MSNBC, and FOX, it seems like politics is a focal point of frustrations for many Americans

I'm here to tell you, "Stop it! It's doing you no good!"

Think about the last time you complained about politics. Did anything change for you? Did your complaining bring about a change in politics? I'm willing to bet good money that it didn't. Unless you are close to one of the politicians or a lobbyist, your complaining about politics will get you nowhere.

If you really want to make a difference in a political campaign, I suggest you either get a job with a cause, volunteer for a cause, or donate to a cause. Sitting your fat—and very dimpled—ass on the edge of your moth-eaten sofa and swearing at the television doesn't count as making a difference in politics.

Imagine playing a sport where you never won or a hobby where you never succeeded. You'd probably either quit or find a way to get a lot better. You would do something. You would take action. It would be stupid of you to do anything else. You would be wasting your time complaining and hoping your situation would change.

That's the same thing with politics. Unless you actively make changes, it won't change the way you want it to change. You have no control over politics.

Stop putting so much importance on government

While the government does have a lot of control over many aspects of our lives, it doesn't control everything. We give too much power to our government. Our government has some say over the homes we buy, the cars we drive, etc. But not nearly as much as people think. [PLEASE NOTE: This was written BEFORE the complete lockdowns due the pandemic. My views have certainly changed regarding the influence our government has over us.]

The little things in your life are not dictated by the government. You can choose to be happy. You can choose to ignore the government. You don't have to bow your head to the government. We don't live in China or Russia. You do have some choices—if you decide to open your eyes to see them.

Don't give the government so much power. You will be much happier. People who protest in this country are out of their minds. The world is mystified by our protests. We have so much for which to be grateful. Quite frankly, I'm mystified.

Conclusion

I could write a whole book about how the news is causing so much anxiety among people, but I want to give you an overview. There is a lot to say on this topic. Just remember that the news causes anxiety in people. However, there are different levels of anxiety. Some people are hardly affected, and some people are greatly affected.

You may not think you are affected, but if you have heart palpitations, you should try giving up the news for a while. I guarantee you will feel a lot better. I know I did.

Just remember, the news makes a ridiculous amount of money by keeping you in fear. Is this something you really want to support? Is this really healthy for you and our society? Do you still want to live in fear and scarcity your whole life?

Key takeaways

- Most news is irrelevant to your life
- The news is in the business of making money
- The news keeps you tuned in by capitalizing on your most primal instinct—fear
- Don't put so much importance on the government. Vote and get on with your life

-9-

How Demeaning TV is Programming Your Heart

The reason why you have heart palpitations is that you have internal turmoil. When you watch demeaning programming like *Jerry Springer, Maury Povich, The Biggest Loser, The Bachelor,* or *The Apprentice*, you have inner turmoil. Your heart will reflect that.

On one hand, you are cheering for some people, but secretly you are happy that other people lost. Now, people might say, "Isn't that what sports and friendly competition is all about?" True. However, these programs make it a point to humiliate the participants. Sports doesn't (for the most part) conduct itself in this manner.

Sports is all about the ball and the field of play. The participants aren't trying to humiliate each other. In fact, in some sporting contests, a winning team will go out of their way NOT to embarrass the losing side. They will deliberately try not to score extra points if the winning team is winning by too many points. Of course, they do this very discretely; otherwise, it may seem even more humiliating to the losing side.

The TV programs mentioned above aren't the only shows that are demeaning; there are many others. This chapter will explore a few of them.

Sitcoms

I used to love sitcoms; they made me laugh. However, as I got older, I realized how condescending they could be. They often pit one person or group against another for the sake of a laugh. It's unfortunate.

There is always someone who is the butt of some tasteless joke. Do you remember Rerun from *What's Happening?* He was the recipient of many fat jokes. And so was Shirley. What about George Costanza from *Seinfeld?* He was the butt of all the bald jokes. I could go on and on, but is this how you want to view the world?

Can you imagine what that does to your well-being? Laughing at those jokes will create inner unrest for you. If you're young, it's fine. But when you get to be older and wiser, your subconscious mind will wonder what's wrong with you. Ultimately, this inner turmoil will manifest in harmful ways.

I'm not saying you can't enjoy television and watch some sitcoms, but you should seriously evaluate what you are watching and what you are laughing at. Belittling someone else doesn't make you bigger. When you laugh at other people's expense, your subconscious knows it is wrong. This will play havoc on your heart. I know this all too well.

Reality Shows

These shows are anything but reality. They warp reality. These shows are often heavily edited to give you their version of events. They are warped and mess with your mind. They make some scenes seem better than they are, and they make other scenes seem far worse than what really happened.

Sadly, real people in these shows do get hurt emotionally. Meanwhile, we are supposed to sit back and be entertained by all this. It may seem entertaining, but ultimately, it makes your heart go cold and black. This was my experience. It caused a lot of inner turmoil for me, and I felt terrible for these people.

The producers of these reality shows claim that these shows are "unscripted." However, everyone can see from the formulaic episodes that these shows are *heavily* scripted.

These shows turn us into sideshow observers—laughing at people's misfortune. The producers are manipulating us into being cold-hearted people. Even contest shows like *American Idol* are scripted. Every punch line is arranged for the right moment. There is nothing organic about these shows. They are a total manipulation of your mind, and your heart is screaming out in protest. It is time to sit back and listen to your heart.

Survivor

This show was about as far from surviving on an island as one can get. People get "voted off" the island because the other "survivors" didn't like them. How is that surviving? This show was heavily scripted, manipulating you to think in a certain way.

Is that how you want to live your life? Do you want the TV to shape your thinking? I don't.

This show only heightens the anxiety that many people have about fitting in with a group of people. For many, this brings back painful memories of high school. However, those memories don't surface because this show is entertainment and takes place on a deserted island. What ends up happening is that those painful memories of high school get suppressed.

This is what causes anxiety and heart palpitations. When you ween yourself off—or hopefully quit cold turkey—from reality shows, you will notice a lifting of your heart. I know I did, and it was one of the best decisions I ever made. These shows cause too much turmoil. There is very little entertainment going on.

The Bachelor

The Bachelor is another show where we are recliner voyeurs and asked to play critic. This show brings up painful memories of being rejected. Yet, we don't acknowledge those painful memories because they are presented in an entertaining way. We are continually saying or thinking, "I'm glad it's her/him and not me."

These emotions and painful memories of being rejected get suppressed. This is what causes bodily pains and heart palpitations.

Jerry Springer, Jenny Jones, etc.

Some shows can be downright humiliating for contestants. Many years ago, there was a *Jenny Jones* episode of a gay man who was in love with his neighbor. In that episode, the audience cheered when they heard that a gay man was going to reveal his crush on another man who was not gay. This straight man was so humiliated by the public gesture that he killed the gay man a few days later.

How do you think those audience members felt when they heard the news? Not too good, I'm sure. Yet, this is supposed to pass as entertainment. This book isn't about how we should classify television; it is a book on how you can heal your heart.

For some reason, many of us like gawking at the misery of others. I'm guilty of it more times than I'd like to admit. However, once I recognized this about myself, I began to change my ways. Deep down, my heart was telling me something wasn't right with how I viewed the world and how I viewed other people in it. Many people talk about a guilty conscience or that their "conscious is getting to them." The reality is that it's the subconscious that's feeling guilty. It comes to the surface from time to time. You may feel it in your consciousness at times. However, your subconscious always feels it.

Your subconscious is not sometimes feeling it like your consciousness is. Your subconscious is always on. You just don't know about it.

The big lesson

The more that you point the finger and laugh at someone else, the more that you will think that people are laughing at you.

I used to feel super self-conscious about how I looked. I would look at myself in the mirror in about twenty different angles. I would look at the back of my head (I always got a bad haircut),

I would look at my profile (I started to see a second chin), I would look at the top of my head (I was thinning), I would put a mirror below my face (maybe my nostrils were too big, too small, too wide, too round, or not round enough, etc.).

This only made me more self-conscious. Finally, I told myself that I can only look in the mirror from the front. That's where I would see people's expressions if I had a booger, a zit, a crumb, etc. If they were looking at the back of my head and having unkind thoughts, I wouldn't know about it. So, who cares?

I was very neurotic. This, of course, does what? Contributes to my anxiety and heart palpitations! And what is the cause of all this? You guessed it, demeaning programming on TV. Not only does it remind you—if only subconsciously—of all your frailties, but it also plants the idea that other people can be critical of such trivialities.

If you never watch those shows, you will go through life blissfully confident regardless if other people would have such thoughts. This is the way it should be.

Bullying

Watching these shows and making comments from your recliner can be considered a form of bullying.

A note about bullies: Bullies are super insecure people. That's not just a happy-go-lucky or pie-in-the-sky way of looking at bullies. It's the truth. Confident people don't need to belittle other people. Whenever I feel the need to put someone down or make comments, I come to realize that I am very insecure about myself.

As I have said repeatedly in this book, don't act on these steps because it will be good for humanity or that maybe you even want to be a better person. Do it solely and selfishly because it will help you get over your heart palpitations. No one will fault you for that. They might. But so, what? This is your survival.

This is your time to be incredibly selfish with the actions you take. Sure, the actions you take with this lesson will have far-reaching benefits than just helping your heart. Make sure you focus on what matters, which is to get you to 100% cured of your heart palpitations.

One of the worst types of shows are the plastic surgery make-over shows. Fox's *The Swan* and ABC's *Extreme Makeover* come to mind. These shows are reprehensible.

After watching these shows, you end up asking yourself:

> "Is my nose too big? Do my ears stick out? Are my eyes too far apart? Is my penis too small? Or too big? God forbid that it's too big. Should my penis look like an acorn sitting on a bean bag? Do my knees look like Idaho potatoes? Are my tits too big, too small, too saggy, too perky, the wrong color, the wrong shape, the wrong [fill in whatever you want here]? Is my ass too saggy or not saggy enough? And what about my elbows? Can I get those buffed and polished?"

As you can see, if you look hard enough, you can have some severe body image issues by watching these reality TV shows. You have only one life to live! Don't live it for someone else. Live it for yourself.

One more time, guess what?

This all plays into your anxieties. This contributes to your heart palpitations. Let's be clear. Your worries can be very subtle on the conscious level. It's more unconscious than you think. Like I said in my last book, I didn't have any real outward signs of anxieties or panic attack symptoms. I didn't feel all doom and gloom. Or dark forebodings. However, I did have heart palpitations.

My anxiety was subconscious. That's the bad part. When your worries seep into your subconscious, that's when you start having all sorts of heart palpitations. You will see in a later chapter how I discovered how much the subconscious plays a role in your heart palpitations.

Big mirror in the sky

The mirror isn't really in the sky. It's all around you. Your life is a mirror. If you watch demeaning TV shows and laugh at people and their frailties, life will reflect that upon you. You will begin to feel, subconsciously, that other people are laughing at you.

When you watch shows like *Survivor*, you begin to question how you can get along with people without them *voting you off*. And you will question how you can socialize in a group without being ridiculed. You will start to wonder if everything you do is acceptable to others. It's enough to make you half-crazy and suffer from debilitating heart palpitations that keep you up at night. Oh, wait, that's exactly what's going on.

Look, I'm not saying there aren't a few valuable lessons that you couldn't learn from *Survivor*. I'm sure there was a moment or two when you said, "You know what, the next time I have a coconut in my hand, maybe I shouldn't do that." However, the reality is that this show is doing more damage to your psyche than it is helping with social mores.

It's tough enough to deal with your workplace and get along with people. Now, you have the added pressure of all the shit that is going on inside your head. It got in there through demeaning television programs like the *Survivor* and *The Bachelor*. Because... how else did it get in there?

Who needs that?

It's not worth it--especially when you have incapacitating heart palpitations. You don't need that. You don't need your nerves on edge with your condition. Realty TV shows and demeaning programs put you on edge. You don't need to have your heart go crazy and feeling like you're going to die. Do you?

When you judge other people, your subconscious believes that other people are judging you. The fear of judgment from other people is a learned trait. It doesn't fall from the sky. You learned this fear of judgment and retribution from somewhere.

Read that carefully. Notice that I said, "the fear of judgment." I didn't say, "judgment."

There are two ways you can fear the judgment of other people. One is to experience it yourself. The other is to learn about it from the media, parents, or friends. The bottom line, it's learned. You're NOT born with this.

However, when you learn it from your own experience, it's put into context. You are learning/fearing it through your personal experience. You can set your meaning to it. In other words, you can judge how serious their judgment is based on your own experience.

When you are being judged through the lens of someone who has watched a lot of reality TV (like *Survivor*), you will take their judgment a lot more seriously. For instance, if you never watched television or media, and someone said you had a funny-looking nose, you might take that as a compliment.

However, after watching surgery shows like *The Swan* or *Extreme Makeover*, or shows like *The Bachelor*, you will take that remark a lot more seriously. You will have no real context in which that remark was made.

This will only heighten your anxiety. That will cause you more heart palpitations. Do you want that? I didn't think so. Do yourself a favor—like I did—and stop watching those demeaning television shows. This includes reality TV, daytime TV, and sitcoms.

Conclusion

When you stop critiquing people on television, you will stop thinking that people are critiquing you. It's that simple. When you feel that people are no longer judging you, you will have removed one more element of your anxiety. And remember, most of your anxiety is subconscious. You may not *feel* panicky, but inside you are. Your heart is telling you the truth. Listen to it.

Key takeaways

- Refrain from watching sitcoms on television
- Life is a big mirror. What you judge will be judged upon you
- Shows like *Survivor* make you question your behavior
- Shows like *Extreme Makeover* make you question your appearance

-10-

Watching These Self-Help Videos May Be Harmful

According to the gurus on YouTube, it seems as if whatever you are doing, you are doing it wrong! Let's not forget that they are all out to make a buck. And they all have their little quirks. This means that they are highly adapted to whatever they are promoting—which ends up being extremely difficult for everyone else. I will explain this in more detail.

While there is a lot of great information on YouTube about health and wellness, there is a lot that can really psyche you out. One thing that really caused me problems was that I was apparently breathing the wrong way. Most yoga practices tell you to do heavy breathing. Even Wim Hof, also known as *The Ice Man*, has a technique where you hyperventilate.

After doing some research, I started to do the Buteyko method of breathing, and it worked. However, now I feared breathing heavily again. In my last book, I talked about how putting tape over my mouth helped me with my heart palpitations. I'm convinced that it worked; however, I still don't know what to think when it comes to proper breathing.

Should I take deep breaths like the yoga teachers? They all say the same thing. Maybe they do know that they are talking about.

Should I hyperventilate like the Ice Man, *so I can brave frigid temperature and make my body immune to all sorts of ailments?*

Should I breathe slowly and lightly, trying to build up CO2, as the great Russian doctors suggested?

It all seems so confusing.

I know from personal experience when I did breathe heavily, my heart would skip a lot more. When I did control my breathing, my heart was calmer. I'm not really debating what works better for someone like me who has heart palpitations. My frustration is that all the information is so conflicting. No one has a concrete answer.

With so much conflict and frustration, it only causes more stress. It may be an excellent time to not seek out so much health information on YouTube.

So much confusion

According to Dr. Gundry, you can't eat tomatoes and peppers because they have lectin. Lectin? Where the hell did that come from?

You can't eat squash, legumes (beans, peas, lentils, peanuts). As mentioned before, nightshade vegetables like tomatoes, peppers, eggplant, and potatoes are off the menu according to YouTube guru, Dr. Gundry. What the hell? So much for a vegan diet. This was making me crazy.

Also, I can't eat corn or meat from corn-fed animals. Even some kinds of milk are off-limits. This was really messing with my head.

According to another YouTube favorite, Dr. Lustig, I can't eat honey, maple syrup, some grains, baked potatoes, coconut oil, BBQ sauce, etc.

Dr. Berg, another YouTube star, tells me I can't eat bread, oatmeal, pasta, etc. What. The. Hell?

I could list about a dozen other doctors on YouTube that were telling me that I am putting my health at significant risk if I eat a particular food. Really? Do you know what's putting my health at considerable risk? YouTube doctors and their crazy diets! Stress is *the* thing that's shortening my life.

What are we supposed to do? This is enough to make you go crazy and have high anxiety. This is why I've adopted a policy of not watching any more health-related stuff on YouTube. The confusion will only cause me to question my sanity.

I must remember something that I mentioned in an earlier chapter. All these gurus/doctors on YouTube are just trying to make money. Nothing wrong with that. I'm not asking for a national protest. Everyone has a right to make money; however, I just choose to ignore them.

If you ignore my advice, this is what you are up against:

- Don't eat ham; you will clog your arteries.
- Don't eat bread; you will spike your insulin.
- Don't eat soy sauce; you will raise your blood pressure.

- Don't eat white rice. Eat brown rice.

As you can see, there is a lot of conflicting information as to how you should eat for long and healthy life. It's not just YouTube. There are hundreds of books by well-respected doctors who are on completely different sides of the equation. At least with books, you will get the full story. With YouTube videos, you are just getting bite-sized clips without the context that you would get from a full-length book.

I'm not against YouTube. I love YouTube because you can find anything on YouTube. This is a blessing and a curse. According to numerous videos on YouTube, I'm apparently doing the following all the wrong way:

- Tying my shoes
- Walking
- Breathing
- Drinking water
- Eating mangoes
- Eating avocadoes

These are just a few of the videos that I can think of off the top of my head that was telling me that I was doing it all the wrong way. There were plenty of other videos showing me that whatever I was doing was completely wrong. How does this make me feel? It makes me feel like I'm doing everything wrong. Does this raise my anxiety level? My angst? My inferiority? Yes, it does!

YouTube is great, but you should be careful about the well-meaning people who are trying to help you with every aspect of your life. I watched one video of a man telling me that I've been tying my shoes the wrong way all my life. He had a better technique. Somehow, my method wasn't good enough. This made me shrink inside. Another man told me I was walking the wrong way. Who knew? Now, whenever I walk down the street, I wonder if I'm screwing up my posture because I'm "walking the wrong way."

Some of them are well-meaning, but it can go too far. I learned I was breathing the wrong way, so that helped. But then there a million videos telling me I'm not drinking enough water. There is an equal number of videos showing me that I'm drinking too much water. What the hell?

Conclusion

Look, I'm not saying these videos aren't helpful. They are. I know how to cut an avocado into chunks without taking off the skin. That's good. However, sooner or later, this stuff can make you a bit neurotic. And that's just the simple stuff. I didn't bother to mention the heavy things like taxes, leaky roofs, pesticides, and so on.

This should go without saying but stay away from all the negative videos that include politics, "fail" videos, accident videos, celebrity bashing videos, etc. No matter what side of the political spectrum you're on, it's probably a good idea to stay away from anything that involves President Donald Trump. It will only make you more agitated. And that is not good for your heart.

Again, what you put into your brain will affect your heart. The more confusion and toxic the material, the more you will manifest the anxiety in some way. Some people break out in bad skin problems. You and I get heart palpitations.

You are better off reading a full-length book on the subject. If it is important enough, then someone will have written a book about it. I haven't come across too many books about tying my shoes or cutting a mango the correct way.

Key takeaways

- Too much conflicting information on YouTube
- YouTube doesn't show full context—books are better
- Limit the videos about diet, health, and well-being

-11-

Ignore Celebrity Gossip

Sadly, in this world, we have a fascination with our celebrities. It's a sickness. We like to kick them when they're up and kick them when they're down. Sounds like a song I once heard about doing my dirty laundry.

When you participate in this gossip, you are comparing yourself to someone whom you think has an ideal life. When it's revealed that they don't have a perfect life, you shit all over it.

This basically sums up celebrity gossip.

Gossiping about someone no matter who is on the receiving end can be considered bullying. You may not be public about it, and you may not direct it toward the celebrity in question. However, by buying the magazines, visiting the websites, and chatting about it, you are supporting the market that makes money on celebrity gossip.

It's unhealthy for you because you are comparing yourself to them in a harmful way. These celebrities have lives that most people will never have. The irony is that most people wouldn't want those lives either, but somehow, they are still jealous and envious.

Most people don't want the life of a celebrity. They don't want all the attention. They don't want all the cameras following them around all the time. If this is you and you still participate in celebrity gossip, you may be stirring up some internal turmoil. This inner turmoil is affecting your heart.

Much like watching the news about all the bad things in the world that you don't want to happen, celebrity gossip is just as bad. You secretly relish in all the bad things that happen to celebrities because you don't think that they deserve the success they have.

Did they get lucky?

Boy bands like Back Street Boys and Insync were manufactured by a record label. They didn't grind it out with instruments in their parents' garages. For many people, they are undeserving of the success they have. They just got lucky.

Justin Bieber is just a pretty boy. He doesn't deserve that success. He just got lucky.

Do you see how celebrity gossip breeds envy and contempt for people you don't even know? They haven't yet done anything to you. It's perfectly reasonable to be mad at Taylor Swift [or Lady Gaga, Madonna, etc.] for canceling a concert because she didn't sell enough seats. But don't be mad at her because she's pretty, and it seems success came to her too easily.

There is no doubt that celebrities throw it in your face by prancing around on late-night talk shows. Guess what? Don't watch late-night talk shows.

Late-night talk shows

If there was one thing I did when I was young that really started to change things for me, it was that I stopped watching late-night talk shows. At that time, there was David Letterman, Johnny Carson, and Conan O'Brien.

The amount of time I wasted watching those silly shows is painful for me to acknowledge. If I only knew better. This was long before YouTube, Netflix, iPhones, etc. Today, I can't figure out why those shows still exist. It's a sad statement about our society. Why there is such a need to watch celebrities bragging about themselves is inconceivable to me. There are better things to do with your life. It's called living your life.

If you want your heart to get better, you must get rid of this toxicity. Celebrity gossip is one of the toxins that's wreaking havoc on you subconsciously. You may not know it, but your heart does. The best thing to do is to just ignore celebrity gossip.

Bad plastic surgery

People love to comment on how celebrities look. This creates anxiety in you on a subconscious and even a conscious level. The more you criticize people, the more you think people are criticizing you.

If you have anxiety about how you look, then you might criticize and analyze how other people look. In turn, you will have more anxiety about how you look because you are picking other people apart. It's a vicious cycle.

When it comes to celebrities, you are dealing with the gold standard for beauty. You will never compete on that level—even if you were the homecoming queen.

The sad thing about plastic surgery is that it's all external. And often, it doesn't truly satisfy people. This is why there is a plastic surgery addiction. Michael Jackson is a prime example.

How does this affect you? The more negative criticism that celebs receive from the public about plastic surgery or any cosmetic enhancement, the more you think about your whole beauty and how you fit into this world. You may not realize it, but you are internalizing it subconsciously. I know this all too well.

Aging

You will age whether you like it or not. If you analyze celebrities on how they age, you will take that internally. I've seen the comments on YouTube, Facebook, Twitter, and Instagram. It's not pretty.

While there's more pressure for women than it is for men to look good, we all must accept that we won't look as good as we age. When we get old, we will look quite disgusting. We'll have lines, creases, folds, warts, moles, skin tags, polyps, boils, age spots, veins, wrinkles, scabs, crusts, fungus, lumps, bumps, bulges, growths, protrusions, you name it. We will all get old, and it won't be pretty. It *will* happen. Live with it and deal with it. Don't scour the Internet to see how celebrities look at your age.

The sooner you accept the ugliness of aging, the sooner you can begin to heal your heart palpitations and live the life you always wanted. I know it worked for me. In high school and college, I was a good-looking guy. However, in my 50's, I started to see the fine lines of aging. Young girls don't look at me like they used to—and they shouldn't. My conscious (subconscious) mind took a long time to accept this reality.

Much of my lack of acceptance in my forties was that I looked at aging celebrities. It made me depressed. We didn't have the Internet back then, so seeing pictures of aging celebrities wasn't readily available. I didn't read *People* or *National Enquirer* for the very reason I wrote this book. I didn't want to get a warped sense of reality.

Now, it's not hard to see celebrities aging. Just the other day, I was searching for information about *Star Wars*. Right in my face, I saw the aging faces of Princess Leia, Luke Skywalker, and Han Solo. (Yeah, I know those are the characters and not the actors, but I still like to think of them that way). Seeing their aging faces made me think about my own aging and mortality.

Now, I know that everyone gets older, and that is a very reasonable thing. What I'm trying to say here is that there is a difference between seeing aging celebrities and having a running commentary on social media on how they are aging.

I know people get older. My parents got older, and I accepted that. But it seems that it's open season on celebrities. The public feels a need to comment on whatever physical deficiencies they have. Don't participate in this circus. It's not good for you.

I know you will have a hard time believing me, but all this media toxicity will play a role in how your heart behaves. It's your subconscious mind at work. Your mind is 95% subconscious and 5% conscious. That's how you can do so many things without thinking about doing them—like driving a car.

Misfortune

Many people relish in the troubles of celebrities, and they are envious of what the stars have. They are glad when something bad happens to a celebrity.

And other people are very saddened by the misfortunes that befall celebrities. When a celebrity's child dies unexpectedly, everyone feels sad. While this is normal to feel sad but is this how you want your life to be? You already have enough people in your life to care for and feel worried about. Do you need to be saddened for people you don't know?

Following celebrities only adds to your mental burden. Your heart palpitations are the result of this burden. As previously mentioned, this psychological burden can manifest itself in many ways. Some people get skin diseases, some get cancer, and some get heart palpitations. It's all the same, and it comes from a mind full of toxicity.

Divorce

Celebrity marriages and divorces give a warped sense of our own realities. Celebrities are always upgrading themselves. When Paul Hogan of *Crocodile Dundee* got famous, he dumped his frumpy wife. Jim Carrey dumped his first wife after becoming famous. Howard Stern dumped his wife for a trophy wife after his career took off. Celebrities love to upgrade their spouses.

This sets a bad example for everyone else and creates a negative vibe in our hearts. You may often think, "Maybe I should dump my wife. Jim Carrey did it. That's not a bad idea." Or "Maybe I could get a new husband. Elizabeth Taylor had seven. Maybe I should have a few more." Or "Maybe I should have sex with my maid. Arnold Schwarzenegger did it. Why not me?"

Conclusion

Do you see how following celebrities and participating in the celebrity gossip cesspool can influence your mind and your well-being? If you are having a lot of heart palpitations, take a good look at your viewing habits and online behavior. Are you idolizing celebrities too much? Are what they are doing in their daily lives dictating how you feel on a day to day basis? When you take a moment and reflect upon this, you may realize how the relationship with celebrities is unhealthy. Try taking a break from looking at celebrities and all the gossip that surrounds them.

Key takeaways

- Ignore celebrity gossip
- Stop comparing yourself to celebrities
- Take a break from celebrity news
- Don't be like Arnold, Jim, or Howard

-12-

Think Way Beyond Yourself for Everlasting Joy

Ever since I had my chronic heart palpitations, I had been on a spiritual journey. I've been asking a lot of questions. Without getting into all the details, here's what my journey has done for me. I no longer fear what I eat. When I was vegan, I feared fat and artery-clogging foods. I feared meat and protein. When I was on Keto, I got over my fear of fat, protein, and cholesterol. But I began to fear sugar. I literally was having the hardest time eating because of my worries.

Since I had been on my spiritual journey, I fear death less and less. And I think this is contributed majorly to the cessation of my heart palpitations.

I'm in a place where I know this life is for me. It's a good life, but it won't last forever. When it ends, that's okay. I'm not gonna get all fearful about it.

Why not?

When I think of the alternatives, I ask myself, why not? Why not be spiritual? What difference does it make? Do I really need to live in the real world where I'm right all the time? Do I need to live in the real world where I need everyone to understand me and my problems? Do I really need to live in a world where I am minding everyone else's business? Do I really need to live in a world that is ruled by TV and celebrities?

I need to live in a world where I am happy. One thing I learned very recently is that if I didn't love myself, I couldn't love anyone else. I now realized why it was so hard to have a loving relationship with other people. Yes, there were other people in my life that I cared for, but did I love them? No, I was too busy worrying about me and my own problems. I didn't love myself. How could I possibly love someone else? I put on a good act for appearance's sake, but was the love there? Not really.

I now realize how easy it is to overcome my heart palpitations, and I now know why they were brought on. My heart was aching. It wasn't an illness; all those doctors were right. It was all in my head, but I wasn't listening.

Death

When I was on a vegan diet, I read all sorts of books on what to eat and what not to eat. I learned so much about what's gonna kill me and what's gonna give me cancer. I was scared to death to eat anything except what they were recommending.

When I went on the Keto diet, I said, "Screw it. If these eggs and bacon kill me, so be it." I really was at my wit's end. I was asking for death to come to me. I was so fed up with all the fearmongering. And then the more I got into the Keto diet, there was more fearmongering. Then I gave up that and said, "Screw it, I will eat whatever I want."

And now I do. I've been eating cold-cut deli sandwiches for the past six months for lunch. According to the vegans, I should be dead or deathly ill from all the roast beef, ham, and cheese I've been eating. According to the Keto people, I should be dead or have diabetes from all the bread I've been eating.

I am not dead, and I don't feel anything close to being deathly ill. And if I am deathly sick, "Screw it, I don't care anymore!" This is my life. No one else's. Who cares what I eat?

I believe people are deathly ill because of what's between their shoulders, not so much what they are eating. Stress is a significant cause of death. A lot of these diets are big on fearmongering. In one book about plant-based foods, they revealed a study where World War I veterans had clogged arteries despite being thin. The book was trying to make this case that you don't have to be fat to be unhealthy and have heart disease.

When I read that so many years ago, it all made sense. What they conveniently left out was that war is incredibly stressful! Maybe—just maybe—all that stress caused those clogged arteries for those soldiers and not their meat-centric diets. Maybe—just maybe. I'm just throwing that out there. I don't really know. What I do know is that stress has done me no good in terms of my heart palpitations. Applying everything I said in this book has done wonders for me.

Since I've been on my spiritual path, I feel so much better about everything, and my heart palpitations are gone.

Stop wishing things would different

One of the things that has helped me on my spiritual journey is to let things go. Let all circumstances be okay. When I had my severe heart palpitations, I was continually wishing things would be different, and it didn't help matters.

It wasn't until I let go and let everything be okay that I felt things get better. It's a scary proposition wishing things to be the same. We want change. You might think those things will be the same if you want them to be. But your subconscious mind is much more sophisticated than that.

Your subconscious mind knows that you want things to be different. But your subconscious mind also wants you to relax and accept things as they are. Once you accept things as they are, you will begin to relax. And once you relax, your heart palpitations will dissipate. I promise you that. You must accept your circumstance and be okay with it, and you must stop resisting.

Stop resisting

We all have resistance. We oppose the way things are. We resist our current circumstances. As mentioned before, what you resist persists. Take a moment now and think about all things you have been resisting. Take inventory of those things.

I was resisting a lot of things. I was resisting that I was a failure in my career. I was resisting that I was a rotten husband. I was resisting wanting to be out with people. Taking note of these things helped me reduce the tension.

I learned not to be afraid of being wrong. I figured I had this one life to live, and I needed to stop resisting the inevitable.

People want to live forever, so they go on all sorts of diets and modalities to extend life. I tried that, too. I tried intermittent fasting and calorie restriction. For what? I wasn't really enjoying myself. We were put on this earth to enjoy ourselves and feel abundant. Making yourself miserable to extend your life doesn't seem to fall into nature's plan.

Acceptance

You need to accept where your life is right now. This is where you were meant to be. Everything up until now brought you to this point. You may not know why, but there is a reason. You may be going through a very tough time right now—especially with your heart palpitations. You need to accept that this is the way it is.

Remember this quote: "What you resist, persists."

I found this to be perfectly accurate. The more I resisted things going on in my life, the more they persisted. Everything from being broke to my relationships with family and friends.

Of course, I noticed this very discreetly with my agonizing heart palpitations. It wasn't until I really accepted myself and how my life turned out was I able to feel like I was getting closer to a cure.

Don't feel like you should be further along than where you are now. This brings about a sense of lack. When you feel lack, you are further away from your goals. Feel abundant and accept things as they are. Once you do, you will feel that your life will progress quickly.

This is precisely why I wrote what I did in this book. The mainstream media will only make you feel lousy about your life, and that's what it's designed to do. If you go on a media diet, you will significantly improve your life and greatly improve your health. I promise that you will see your heart palpitations go away.

Patience

The one thing that hindered my cure was my lack of patience. I was very impatient. I wanted my condition to be resolved right away. Every single day that I had to deal with my health was another day of frustration. I had no patience for any kind of long-term cures. I wanted it now.

I overdosed on magnesium and CoQ10 so I could resolve my issue fast. I had no patience to see things through.

You must have patience in whatever you decide to do. You must have patience in what I am telling you is going to work. One of the biggest regrets in my life is that I didn't have enough patience for anything. I left jobs because I wasn't paid enough. Unfortunately, it was right before things started getting good. The companies I left had gotten new accounts, and everyone got a raise. I left too soon.

I broke up with girlfriends because things weren't going fast enough. I was impatient. My lack of patience was the ruin of me.

Be patient with what I am telling you. I see people on Facebook groups who want a quick fix to their problems. They want a "secret" or a pill. They don't want to hear from someone like me who cured himself nearly 100% over six months. I was like that, too. And that impatience delayed my cure for three years.

The world needs more patience

Unfortunately, as a society, we're getting less patient day by day. As we get technology that gets us stuff faster and faster, we have less and less patience. We don't want to wait any longer.

With marketing messages telling us we can lose seven pounds in seven days or make a million dollars in six months, it's no wonder we are impatient. We want our stuff now!

But I am going to tell you now, you must have patience. You must trust that what I am telling you will work, and it will have a long-lasting effect. Isn't that what you want?

Accept change

The world is changing all the time. If you cannot accept the change, you will go mad. This reminds me of the time when I heard someone talking about her vacation experience.

A woman I knew from Wisconsin had read about Nantucket Island in a high-end lifestyle living magazine. After her family vacationed Nantucket for a few years, she was disappointed because it had been "discovered." She said, "Now, everyone is coming here." She was depressed that it was no longer her secret hideaway. She couldn't accept change. Change will always happen, so you might as well get used to it.

People are afraid of AI (artificial intelligence), driverless cars, new technology, etc. These people are resisting. Guess what? AI is gonna happen! The same with driverless cars. There is nothing you can do about it. Worrying about it won't change a thing.

Have gratitude

Be grateful for all the things you already have. This was a big turning point in helping me with my heart palpitations. I never really felt appreciation for what I had. Sure, I loved it (whatever it was) when I got it. Soon after, I got bored with it. I didn't appreciate it any longer. Whether it was furniture, clothes, sporting equipment, cars, etc., I never really enjoyed them to the extent of when I first acquired them. I always found fault with them. I wanted something new.

It saddens me is that so many people who live in the United States don't appreciate what a great country this is. We live in one of the most prosperous countries in the world, and we have everything we could ever want or need. Sadly, too many people are too busy being angry about someone or something—blaming each other about everything.

If you want to resolve your heart palpitations, you must appreciate where you live, no matter what. Once I removed myself from the toxic media and learned to love where I lived, things turned around for me in a big way. In addition to resolving my heart palpitations, I got my dream house. All I need to do is appreciate my current living conditions.

Conclusion

You may think the solution to your heart palpitations is in a pill, at the doctor's office, or on the Internet. But it's really inside you. YOU are the solution. No one is going to solve this problem for you. You must believe that you are the solution to your problem.

For most of us, this problem was created within us. It didn't fall out of the sky. We created this problem. Yes, there could be diet issues and a lack of vitamins and minerals, but mostly it's from our negative attitudes.

And our negative attitudes come mostly from the toxic media we consume each and every day. Not only do we passively absorb this negativity, but now with a soapbox at every click, we stand on it and spew out this same toxicity to everyone.

We're on Facebook complaining about the plight of the world and how unfair everything is. We make fun of the unfortunate (cats don't count), we pick apart celebrities, and we perpetuate the fearmongering stories that the news puts out.

This all gets programmed into your subconscious mind. And then what happens? You suffer from tormenting heart palpitations that scare you to death, and that keep you up all night. Do you really want to live this way? Is this way it's supposed to be?

Key takeaways

- Consider a spiritual journey
- Accept things as they are

- Have patience with yourself
- Have gratitude for all that you have

-13-

A Prescription for Success

Here is my prescription for reducing your heart palpitations. In a review of what I had written in the previous chapters, most people who have heart palpitations have lots of stress and anxiety. However, they may not realize it.

I know I didn't. I thought I was relatively calm. I had some stressors in my life, but I thought they just came and went. I didn't realize that my daily habits were keeping me in fight-or-flight mode. As we get older, the habits we previously tolerated finally catch up to us. Over time, I developed some good habits that help me reduce stress and lower my anxiety.

Morning routine

I do this most mornings. In my other book, I had an hour-by-hour schedule. This prescription is a little less rigid.

What I do:

My alarm is set for 5:00 am, but I usually wake up on my own between 4:30 am – 4:45 am.

What I recommend:

Find a time that works for you and stick to it. Practice good sleep hygiene. This means waking up and going to bed at the same time every single day. This includes weekends. I wake between 4:30 and 5:00 on Saturdays and Sundays. And I go to bed before 10:00 am on Fridays and Saturdays.

Exercise

I start my exercise routine between 5:15 am – 5:35 am, depending on how fast I get moving and whether I go to the gym or not.

I do various exercises either at the gym or at home. These include weights, yoga, treadmills, ellipticals, etc. When I do my workouts, I try to breathe through my nose as much as I can. Of course, when the exercise gets intense, I tend to breathe through my mouth.

(Over breathing will stimulate your parasympathetic nervous system. This nervous system is the one that activates your fight-or-flight mode. This causes anxiety. Anxiety causes over-breathing. It's just one big cycle. It's hard to break. One way to reduce over breathing is to breathe through your nose as much as possible. I go into more detail on over breathing in my other book, so I don't want to rehash it here.)

I exercise on Mondays, Wednesdays, Fridays, and Saturdays. Sometimes, I do my workouts at home. For those exercises, I watch workout videos on my TV and follow along. You can buy almost any kind of video online. When I'm home, I mostly do yoga and bodyweight strength training. I will work out at home if I don't have time to go to the gym and need to get to work early.

Meditation

I try to meditate for about 45 minutes every day. Sometimes, I don't have time. Also, I will alternate days when I exercise and when I meditate. So, following my gym schedule, I will commit to meditating on Tuesdays, Thursdays, Saturdays, and Sundays. Since I have more time on Saturdays, I work out and meditate.

I also meditate in the evenings. I will go into more detail on the evening schedule.

Gratitude Journal

I write in my gratitude journal nearly every day. I write out how grateful I am for everything I have. I developed this practice only a few years ago. So far, it's made me a much happier person. I highly recommend this practice. When we are not grateful for what we already have, we tend to be in the "wanting more" mode.

Also, we are always wanting to be things to be different. I found this to be stressful over time. Always wanting things to be different can be put a lot of stress on your mind. Be happy with who you are and what you have. Stop wanting things to be changed.

Workday

Making lists. I found making lists of things I need to do dramatically reduces my stress. Trying to keep a million items in your head causes a lot of stress and anxiety. I found making lists and crossing things off my list to be fun and relaxing. It makes you feel like you have more control over your life. This is key to helping reduce your stress, anxiety, and heart palpitations.

Don't engage with people who will stress you out. Some are unavoidable, and some are totally avoidable. It's incredible how many people put themselves in stressful situations by choice. Be very conscious of what you are doing throughout the day. Meditations will help you with this.

Media Diet

I make sure not to watch the news or anything upsetting in the evenings. If I do waver from this, it's usually on Friday and Saturday evenings, where I'm not so stressed out from work. I feel more relaxed at home with my family.

If I'm on Facebook and other social media, I make sure to limit it to only a few minutes a day. If I come across posts that are upsetting, I just move on. After about ten minutes, I turn it off. It seems that people are always posting something that is bothering me. It's either my friends telling me how great their life is or someone posting about all the troubles of the world. Either way, after ten minutes, I'm pretty much caught up. I have found that limiting my social media has dramatically reduced my anxiety and stress. This, of course, helped me overcome my heart palpitations.

This media diet includes all media such as TV, social media, newspapers, and books. Periodicals can be especially harmful. I haven't read a newspaper in years, and I still know what's going on in the world. You don't need to read newspapers or watch the news to know what's going on in the world. If it's that important to you and your family, you will find out somehow.

Read

I try to read for at least forty-five minutes every night. It doesn't always happen, but that's my goal. The great thing about books is that you can stop and start any time you want. They are portable, and you can take them anywhere.

I don't read fiction, but when I do, I find them to be relaxing because they take me to some far-off place—something a movie just can't do. By reading books, you are allowing your imagination to create the imagery that is described in the book. Your mind is working. In movies, with all their special effects, your brain doesn't have to do anything. It becomes stale.

Mostly, I read non-fiction. I learned a lot about health and wellness from reading books. Sometimes, I read too much of this and can make me a little stressed. So, I put the book down. Lately, I've been reading biographies of very successful people. This has allowed me to believe that anything is possible. It's very uplifting. It helps me escape from my own problems and will enable me to think that I can get over my personal issues.

What most people don't realize is that heart palpitations are often caused by built-up stress. Reading can be relaxing and can help center yourself.

Evening meditation

Usually, I meditate for about forty-five minutes in the evening. I don't always have time. Or I may choose to watch a movie instead. But I try to fit it in when I can. This has dramatically reduced my stress. After doing this meditation, I feel much calmer and more relaxed.

Bedtime

Most evenings, I go to bed immediately after my meditation. Sometimes, I go to bed after watching a movie.

For one to two hours before going to bed, I don't engage in anything that will force me to take action. It's either reading, meditating, or watching a movie in my recliner for me. Nothing else.

I usually watch a fun show or movie that I know I enjoyed in the past. There is too much pressure to try to experience something new.

I don't use my computer. This engages the mind too much. Using a computer or a smartphone in any way will activate your brain. This is not conducive to sleep. Any other activity that engages my mind is also avoided. I don't engage in any hobbies, messaging, cooking, deep conversations, etc.

It's only meditation, reading, or watching a movie. I specifically say movie because they run more than an hour. I don't want to watch a short television program for less than an hour and then engage my mind to figure out what else to watch or do. I want the last two hours of my evening to be calm, relaxing, and meditative.

A lot of people will cry, "I don't have that kind of time." You will if you make it a priority. I used to think I didn't have that kind of time. You do. If you track what you do in the evenings, you will realize how much time is wasted doing non-essential things.

This evening protocol has allowed me to get a perfect night's sleep in only six or seven hours. If I sleep longer, I get groggy. Like I said in the beginning, I wake up before my 5:00 am alarm. I usually go to bed between 9:30 pm and 10:00 pm.

Breathing

After my evening meditation or instead of my evening mediation, I would do a short breathing exercise. This slows down my breathing. There is a guided exercise by Stephen Elliott, and you can buy the CD or MP3 at www.Coherence.com. I'm not affiliated with them, and I don't make any money from any sales they make. I am just mentioning this because it helped me control my breathing.

Basically, the audio is a kind of metronome to slow down your breathing. Before using this CD, my breathing was around 15 beats per minute. This is just outside of the normal range of 10-14 beats per minute. Using this audio, I was able to reduce my breathing down to 5 beats per minute before going to bed. This has been a massive help to me in overcoming my anxiety and my heart palpitations.

Summary

This is a simple prescription of what I do keep calm and relaxed. So far, it has helped me a great deal with dealing with my heart palpitations. If I waver from this, sometimes I feel a little blip or reminder. When that happens, I get back on track.

Key takeaways

- Go to bed and wake up at the same time every day
- Meditate as often as you can
- Have a schedule to keep things organized
- Write things down to remove them from your mind
- Control your breathing

Thank you for reading this book! If you want to reach out to me for any questions and concerns, please email me at AustinWintergreen@gmail.com

May I ask you a small favor?

If you enjoyed reading this book and would like other people to benefit from the information in this book, could you please review my book on Amazon and/or Goodreads?

Thank you!

Your review will help other heart palpitation sufferers find solutions to their problem. This is what helped me!

Click here to write a review on Amazon

Click here to write a review on Goodreads

Made in the USA
Las Vegas, NV
20 November 2023

81223105R00100